Dear Amina,

Together lets make this planet a better place

Best wishes,

Darryl

Net Zero For Business

For information contact :

Darryl Mattocks
https://www.TheNetZeroForBusinessBook.com

ISBN: 978-1-3999-4985-9

First Edition, June 2023

Publisher ref:NZFB-22-06-23-06P

CONTENTS

AUTHOR'S NOTE

This book is aimed at managers who want to develop a cost-effective and practical plan to reduce the carbon footprint of their organisation. It shows you how to reduce the carbon footprint of your business in a logical, methodical, and practical way. It has been gleaned from helping many companies – large and small – do exactly that over many years.

In this book, I introduce three new ideas:

Firstly, I clarify the term 'Net Zero' – a widely-used phrase in the industry, but one that lacks clear definition.

Secondly, I introduce the concept of 'certification' and 'certified Net Zero'. Certification need not be an overly long or complex process, but the industry needs some better checks and balances around use of the term Net Zero, and certification will help to bring greater clarity.

Thirdly, to make the carbon reduction process more manageable, I have split it into seven simple-to-follow steps which I call the 'MARTOC method'. Apart from the very first step, each component of the MARTOC process will end up being a section of your Carbon Reduction Plan.

The seven steps of the MARTOC method are:

Step 1 – Make several sweeping assumptions to get started on your plan in as short a time as possible. This helps to determine the order of magnitude of your carbon footprint and identify what the key drivers of your emissions are. We call this process the 'Net Zero catapult'.

Step 2 – Measure – Measure your carbon footprint

Step 3 – Aim – Aim to reduce your carbon emissions by a set amount within a given time period

Step 4 – Reduce – Commit to a number of carbon reduction projects to reduce your footprint

Step 5 – Track and revise – Track your progress year on year and, over time, revise the plan if required

Step 6 – Offset and remove - Once you've put plans in place to reduce your footprint, offset any emissions that are left

Step 7 – Certify and commit - Get senior management to sign off on the plan and an external company to check and certify it

Underpinning my definition of Net Zero is the awkwardly named UK-government standard, 'PPN 06/21', which I have extended for the definition of Net Zero to include supply chain emissions. As a standard, it is far from perfect, but it has a large following and it forms a practical and useful basis to build on, adding rigour and credibility to the Net Zero process. As such, the term Net Zero encompasses PPN 06/21, and the terms can be used reasonably interchangeably.

Certified Net Zero' simply refers to a Net Zero plan that has been checked and signed off by a certification agency.

I give enough guidance in this book for you to do your carbon analysis in Microsoft Excel and Word. However, I strongly recommend you consider using an online platform to take the pain out of the process and make developing the plan significantly faster and easier. [1]

---

1 To declare a vested interest, my companies, Enistic and Yeti, have cost-effective online software designed to do this, and occasional references to them are made throughout the book. Other platforms are available, and all examples can be easily replicated with the other software packages. For more information see https://enistic.com/ and https://yeti.org/.

Chapter 1

INTRODUCTION

WHY EVERY BUSINESS SHOULD HAVE A CARBON REDUCTION PLAN

If you're reading this book, you're probably already familiar with some of the dangers of global warming. We've seen floods happening increasingly frequently throughout the world. - severe flooding in Pakistan in 2022 caused billions of dollars worth of damage and killed many people. Meanwhile, huge wildfires in California and Australia have devastated entire regions. These are sadly just the start of a pattern of increasing frequency of extreme climate-related events, each one subsequently costing billions to clear up, as well as countless lives.

If we don't take action to limit global warming, we may reach a tipping point where it's too late. This book is focussed on simple to implement, practical measures to reduce emissions produced by businesses.

WHAT CAUSES GLOBAL WARMING?

Global warming is caused by a build-up of pollutants in the upper atmosphere. In the past, upon reaching Earth, the heat from the sun would largely bounce back into space. Industrialisation then introduced a growing number of pollutants which began to accumulate in the upper atmosphere and reflect an increasing amount of heat back down to Earth.

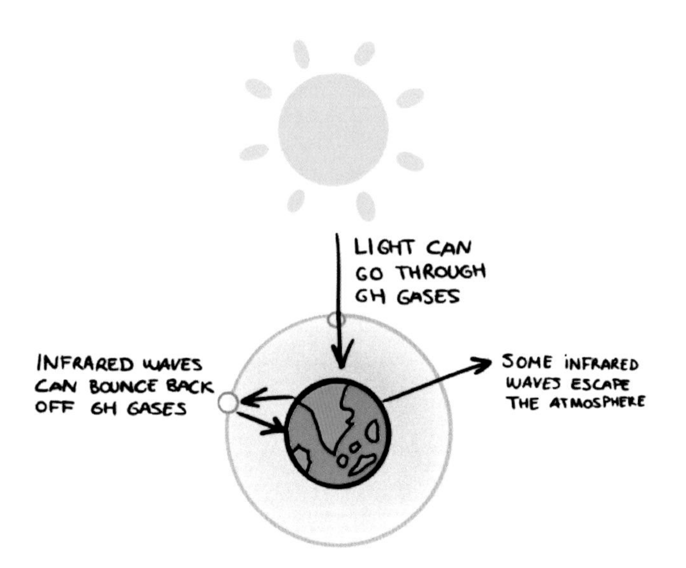

In terms of how much our planet will heat up by, it's hard to say. Scientists were previously predicting an average rise of 1.5˚C, but 2˚C is perhaps now more of a realistic estimate. The question that is often asked when we discuss this is whether 1˚C is a lot. I write this from Oxford in the UK, and the temperature today is a chilly 11˚C. So surely one degree isn't a lot?

On any particular day, in any particular place, 1˚C is not significant. A *global average temperature increase of 1˚C*, however, causes huge changes in global weather patterns, initiating climate chaos. To put things into perspective, the period when we saw global cooling of just 5˚C was what we now refer to as the Ice Age.

It is critical that we keep global warming to 1.5˚C, or 2˚C at the most, for the next few decades. This should buy us enough time to figure out how to remove CO2 from the atmosphere in a cost-effective way and restore balance back to the planet.

> By the time we see that climate change is really bad, your ability to fix it is extremely limited... The carbon gets up there, but the heating effect is delayed. And then the effect of that heat on the species and ecosystem is delayed. That means that even when you turn virtuous, things are actually going to get worse for quite a while.
>
> — *Bill Gates*

NET ZERO MAKES SOUND COMMERCIAL SENSE

We all understand that we should be doing our bit for the good of the planet but being sustainable also makes good commercial sense. Here are the top 10 commercial benefits of achieving Net Zero for your business:

1. **Cost savings**: Companies that reduce their greenhouse gas (GHG) emissions and become Net Zero can save money through reduced energy consumption and operational costs. According to a study by CDP (a charity that runs the global disclosure system for investors, companies, cities, states and regions to manage their environmental impacts), companies that disclosed their emissions reductions in 2018 reported cost savings of $19.3 billion.[i]

2. **Increased revenue**: Customers are increasingly demanding sustainable products and services, and companies that demonstrate a commitment to sustainability can attract more customers and increase their revenue. A global survey by Nielsen found that 81% of respondents felt strongly that companies should help improve the environment[ii].

3. **Improved brand image**: Companies that achieve Net Zero can improve their brand image and reputation, which can increase customer loyalty and attract new customers. A survey by Cone Communications found that 87% of consumers will purchase a product because a company advocated for an issue they cared about[iii].

4. **Competitive advantage**: Companies that lead the way in sustainability can gain a competitive advantage over their peers. A survey by Accenture found that 62% of consumers are willing to pay more for products and services from companies that are committed to reducing their environmental impact[iv].

5. **Regulatory compliance**: As governments around the world implement new regulations to address climate change, companies that become Net Zero can ensure compliance and avoid potential penalties. For example, the European Union's emissions trading system imposes a price on carbon emissions, which can be a significant cost for companies that have not achieved Net Zero[v].

6. **Employee retention and recruitment**: Companies that prioritise sustainability can improve employee morale and retention, as well as attract new talent interested in working for socially responsible companies. A survey by Cone Communications found that 64% of millennials consider a company's social and environmental commitments when deciding where to work[vi].

7. **Improved supply chain**: Companies that achieve Net Zero can also encourage their suppliers to adopt sustainable practices, which can create a more resilient and sustainable supply chain. A survey by CDP found that companies that engage with their suppliers on climate change outperform those that don't, with a 96% higher return on investment[vii].

8. **Risk mitigation**: Achieving Net Zero can also help companies mitigate risks associated with climate change, such as physical impacts from extreme weather events or supply chain disruptions due to resource constraints. A report by the Carbon Trust found that companies that take action on climate change are better equipped to manage future risks and uncertainties[viii].

9. **Investor confidence**: Investors are increasingly looking for companies that are committed to sustainability and reducing their carbon footprint. A survey by Morgan Stanley found that sustainable funds outperformed their traditional counterparts during the COVID-19 pandemic, highlighting the resilience of sustainable investments[ix].

10. **Stepping up**: Business owners should contribute towards carbon reduction, rather than ignore the problem and let other people shoulder the burden. Commercial activities can have a significant impact on the environment and future generations, and by taking proactive steps to reduce their carbon footprint, businesses can not only help address the climate crisis but also gain a competitive edge, attract environmentally conscious customers and save money in the long run.

QUIZ: HOW CARBON SAVVY IS YOUR BUSINESS?

Take the quiz below to assess how carbon savvy your business is.

1. Does your business have a policy in place for reducing its carbon footprint?

- ☐ a) Yes, we have a comprehensive policy in place
- ☐ b) We have some guidelines in place, but they could be improved
- ☐ c) We have considered implementing a policy, but haven't yet
- ☐ d) No, we do not have a policy in place
- ☐ e) I'm not sure

2. How do you dispose of your business waste?

- ☐ a) We recycle as much as possible and dispose of the rest responsibly
- ☐ b) We dispose of all waste in separate landfill and recycling bins
- ☐ c) We donate or repurpose our waste when possible
- ☐ d) We outsource waste disposal to a third-party provider without checking what they do with it
- ☐ e) I'm not sure

3. Do you encourage your employees to use environmentally friendly practices at work?

- ☐ a) Yes, we regularly remind and educate our employees about environmentally friendly practices
- ☐ b) We occasionally encourage our employees to use environmentally friendly practices
- ☐ c) We don't specifically encourage or discourage environmentally friendly practices
- ☐ d) No, we don't think it's necessary or feasible for our business
- ☐ e) I'm not sure

4. Do you use energy-efficient appliances and equipment in your business?

- ☐ a) Yes, we use energy-efficient appliances and equipment throughout our business
- ☐ b) We use some energy-efficient appliances and equipment, but not all
- ☐ c) We don't use energy-efficient appliances and equipment
- ☐ d) We have considered using energy-efficient appliances and equipment, but haven't yet
- ☐ e) I'm not sure

5. Do you use renewable energy sources to power your business?

- ☐ a) Yes, we have already started using renewable energy sources to power our business
- ☐ b) We have thought about using renewable energy sources, but haven't taken any action yet

☐ c) We have investigated using renewable energy sources, but it's not feasible for our business

☐ d) No, we haven't considered using renewable energy sources to power our business

☐ e) I'm not sure

6. Have you implemented any measures to reduce water consumption in your business?

☐ a) Yes, we have implemented multiple measures to reduce water consumption in our business

☐ b) We have implemented some measures to reduce water consumption, but there is room for improvement

☐ c) We haven't implemented any measures to reduce water consumption yet, but plan to in the future

☐ d) No, we have not implemented any measures to reduce water consumption and do no currently have any plans to do so

☐ e) I'm not sure

7. Do you source environmentally friendly products and services for your business?

☐ a) Yes, we actively seek out and source environmentally friendly products and services for our business

☐ b) We occasionally source environmentally friendly products and services, but it's not a top priority

☐ c) We have investigated sourcing environmentally friendly products and services, but they are not available in our area

☐ d) No, we don't specifically seek out or prioritise environmentally friendly products and services

☐ e) I'm not sure

Scoring:

- For every "a" answer, give yourself two points.

- For every "b" answer, give yourself one point.

- For every "c" answer, give yourself zero points.

- For every "d" answer, subtract one point.

- For every "e" answer, give yourself zero points.

What does my score mean?

- 0-3 points: Your business may not be very environmentally aware. Consider implementing some measures to reduce your carbon footprint.

- 4-6 points: Your business is somewhat environmentally aware, but there is room for improvement. Look for ways to further reduce your impact on the environment.

- 7-9 points: Your business is doing well in terms of being environmentally aware. Keep up the good work and continue to explore new ways to reduce your carbon footprint and promote sustainability.

- 10-14 points: Your business is a leader in environmental awareness and sustainability practices. Congratulations on taking significant steps to reduce your carbon footprint and make a positive impact on the environment! Keep sharing your success with others to inspire more businesses to do the same.

If your business has not yet started its carbon reduction journey, it is not uncommon to receive a score at the lower end of the scale. Most of my clients score less than 5 when we start working with them, and over 10 after 12-18 months of efforts.

Chapter 2

AN INTRODUCTION TO NET ZERO

WHAT DO 'NET ZERO' AND 'CARBON NEUTRAL' MEAN?

There are many different definitions of Net Zero and carbon neutral. Researching these terms online produced 18 different definitions, including from the BBC, the United Nations, and the governments of both the UK and overseas. There is no general consensus on what is meant by the two terms (or in one case, 'net carbon neutral'). Some would say that Net Zero is the act of offsetting the emissions from your organisation, whilst others would say it is reducing your carbon to its lowest possible level. A few mentioned both aspects.

The Science Based Targets initiative (SBTi), however, provides a comprehensive definition of Net Zero which centres around reducing carbon use and then offsetting or removing what's left (see box below). Note that the definition does not exclude adding in other aspects to achieving Net Zero; it simply defines the minimum set of components that must be included. If you had, for example, an extensive leasing business, you might logically want to include information on those leases. Similarly, if your business manufactures products that have significant end-of-life disposal needs, you might want to consider that too.

Carbon neutral refers simply to buying offsets to cover emissions, without reducing actual emissions. The term is therefore not useful for the purpose of this book, which is focussed on emissions reduction.

What is 'Net Zero'?

Net Zero refers to the state in which a company has reduced their carbon emissions to the absolute minimum and offset or removed whatever emissions still remain.

How to achieve Net Zero

For a business to achieve Net Zero, a Carbon Reduction Plan must be published annually, showing how it will ambitiously reduce its carbon footprint to the absolute minimum and offset or remove any remaining carbon emissions.

To calculate a business' carbon footprint, emissions from all fuels, electricity, supply chains, business travel, waste, deliveries coming in, deliveries going out, commuting and home working must be included. The accuracy of the supply chain emissions footprint should be at least 60% and all other elements at least 90% accurate.

The plan should be signed off by a senior director and contain explanations of your carbon footprint, your reduction targets, your plans to reduce emissions, historic progress against the targets you have set yourself, and what offsets or removals were purchased. If certification was obtained, details of that certification must be included.

What is 'carbon neutral'?

For a business to be carbon neutral, the quantity of offsets or removals purchased must equal the business' total carbon emissions.

If we compare Net Zero with PPN 06/21 (see below), we can see that Net Zero is an extension of that standard, and all Net Zero companies will therefore automatically be PPN 06/21 compliant.

	PPN 06/21	Net Zero	Certified Net Zero
Produced annually	√	√	√
Targets	√	√	√
Progress tracking	√	√	√
Director sign-off	√	√	√
Publication	√	√	√
Electricity, gas and fuel	√	√	√
Business travel	√	√	√
Waste	√	√	√
Deliveries in	√	√	√
Deliveries out	√	√	√
Commuting	√	√	√

	PPN 06/21	Net Zero	Certified Net Zero
Work from home		√	√
Supply chain		√	√
Offsets and removals		√	√
Certification			√

WHAT IS A CARBON FOOTPRINT?

Your carbon footprint is an approximate measure of the amount of pollutants you emit, either for a specific activity - such as driving from Oxford to Edinburgh - or over a period of time.

Why 'approximate' I hear you ask? Because carbon reporting is more of an art than a science, and no carbon footprint is ever 100% accurate. The more effort you put into establishing the details of your carbon footprint, the more accurate it will be, but all carbon footprints are estimates to one degree or another. As an example, if we ask what the carbon footprint of our drive from Oxford to Edinburgh is, we obviously include the emissions from the petrol we use. But what about the cup of coffee we bought on the way there? What about the lights in the café, the paper used to make the coffee cup or the energy used to roast the coffee beans?

DEFINING THE SCOPE OF A CARBON FOOTPRINT

Unless you have a month of Sundays available to you, we must always draw the line somewhere, and where we draw that line makes a huge difference to our estimated carbon footprint. In our example above, we might decide that we will only include the fuel used for the journey and ignore everything else (which is a very common thing to do), or we might decide to include other aspects, such as the footprint of the coffee. Obviously, by including more components, the estimated carbon footprint is going to be larger, but it is interesting to note that both measures are entirely valid so long as you state the standard that was used when they were calculated.

The way around this is to follow standards that define what it is and is not acceptable to include. There's more on standards later in this book, but some standards, such as the Greenhouse Gas Protocol, define very precisely what should be included, whilst others, such as PPN 06/21, are vaguer and leave it to the company to decide. Whilst many companies boldly claim to follow the Greenhouse Gas Protocol reporting standards, the quality of reporting I've seen claiming to conform to this standard has varied considerably.

In the real world, when you come across statements such as *"Our carbon footprint is X"*, make sure to ask about the scope of this – specifically, what standard was used and what is included and excluded?

Many companies will include their electricity, gas and fuel, but ignore everything else. As 'everything else' can be significant, these footprints are a good start, but misleading in the long run if you want to use them as a basis for truly reducing your environmental impact as a business.

As we saw in our coffee example above, calculating the carbon footprint of what a company buys can be difficult, and many people simply don't bother. If you have an office-based business, this is bad-practice but generally not hugely significant. However, if you are a manufacturer or reseller, it is critical you include your supply chain, as it will likely form the majority of your carbon footprint.

MORE THAN ONE CARBON FOOTPRINT

You may see manufacturers and resellers state two carbon footprints: one for their own operations, over which they have high levels of control; and one for the things they buy in, over which they have less control.

As an example, if your business were based out of a small office on an industrial estate and bought and sold metal (which has a large carbon footprint), it would be good practice to calculate the carbon footprint of the metal you buy in as stock separately from the electricity, heating and travel required to support your internal operations. This would allow you to see the wood from the trees and concentrate on each part of the problem of reducing your carbon footprint independently.

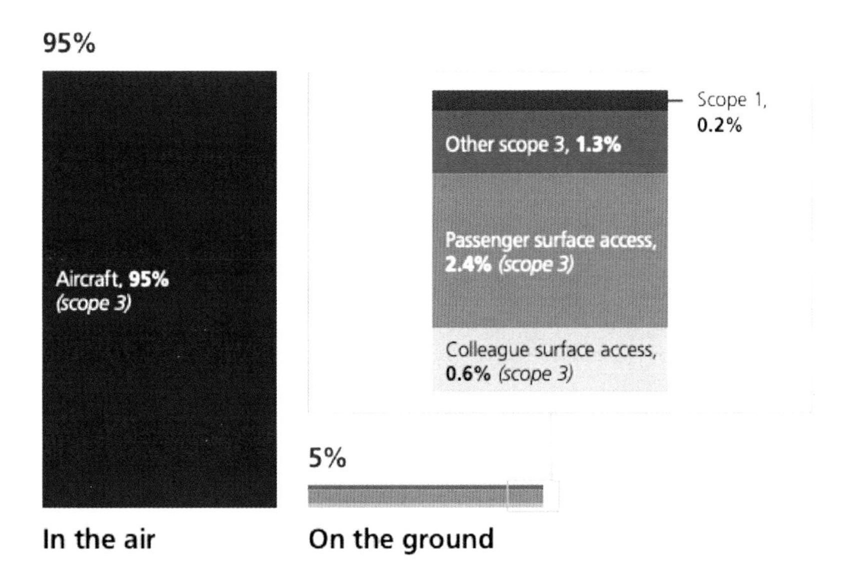

Figure 1: Heathrow Airport's carbon footprint is divided into two sections to allow the organisation to focus on each part of its carbon footprint separately. Source: Heathrow Airport[x].

CARBON FOOTPRINTS CHANGE OVER TIME

When we talk about carbon footprints, we need to remember that they will change from year to year. In an ideal world, they wouldn't, but in reality, they most certainly do, and sometimes significantly.

In the main, this can be attributed to two things. Firstly, companies change size and shape over time – they move in and out of different offices, increase or decrease their staff base, buy or sell subsidiary companies, and so on. All of these changes significantly affect a company's carbon footprint. Secondly, companies tend to need to include more elements in their carbon footprint each year as their internal systems develop, especially when it comes to supply chain.

There are ways to deal with both problems. Carbon intensity metrics will allow you to deal with companies changing size and shape, and the use of standards such PPN 06/21 will reduce the impact of including or excluding different things over time. Either way, however, it is important to accept that carbon footprints can, and do, change over time.

HOW WE MEASURE CARBON EMISSIONS – WHAT IS TCO2E?

The 'tonnes of CO2 equivalent' measurement unit

When we talk about emissions that build up in the atmosphere, there are many different types of pollutants that can gather there and reflect heat back down to the Earth's surface. Some, like carbon dioxide, we've all heard of; others, like sulphur hexafluoride or nitrous oxide, are less familiar.

If we had to consider the entire list of pollutants every time, it would make it difficult to measure and compare carbon footprints, so we condense this long list into just one pollutant: CO2. When using tCO2e, instead of listing each pollutant separately, we therefore equate each one to its respective equivalent amount of CO2 and calculate the total.

As an example, sulphur hexafluoride is nasty stuff. It's one of the refrigerating gases you used to find in old air conditioning systems and fridges. Every tonne of sulphur hexafluoride in the atmosphere has the same heat-reflecting ability of 23,500 tonnes of CO2. So, we say:

A tonne of sulphur hexafluoride is equivalent to 23,500 tonnes of CO2

If we had, therefore, emissions equating to 0.5 tonnes of sulphur hexafluoride from one of our air conditioning units that sprung a leak, we could say:

A leak of 0.5 tonnes of sulphur hexafluoride which is equivalent to 11,750 tonnes of CO_2

This can then be recorded as:

Air conditioning leaks: 11,750 tCO_2e

As a further example, nitrous oxide is emitted from many engines and industrial processes throughout the world, as well as from burning fossil fuels. Each tonne of nitrous oxide is equivalent to 298 tonnes of CO_2, so: 1 tonne nitrous oxide = 298 tCO_2e.

Using the unit tCO_2e as a measurement of your carbon footprint, therefore, allows quick comparisons of different company's carbon footprints and simplifies the carbon reduction problem into one that is manageable.

Visualising a tonne of carbon dioxide

To visualise what a tonne of CO_2 looks like, 1 tonne of CO_2 would roughly fill an Olympic-sized swimming pool.

A typical family household in the European Union will emit approximately one tCO2eper month, or approximately 10 to 12 tonnes a year, and small and medium sized enterprises (SMEs) tend to vary from five to 15 tCO2e per year. A good rule of thumb, therefore, is to think of average emissions per family or per SME of 10 tonnes per year, or roughly one tonne per month[xi].

Larger businesses emit significantly more than this, with the actual amount depending on their size and sector, as you might expect. A lot of the larger businesses will have emissions of 10,000-20,000 tCO2e per year, although there are many at less than 1,000 and a few at over 50,000 tCO2e per year. The largest footprint we've ever dealt with was over seven million tCO2e per year globally. This was a very large multinational company and is the exception rather than the rule.

Company	Annual Emissions
1. Walmart	2020 CO2 emissions: 21.5 million metric tonnes
2. State Grid Corporation of China	2019 CO2 emissions: 1,878.6 million metric tonnes
3. Amazon	2020 CO2 emissions: 60.6 million metric tonnes
4. China National Petroleum Corporation	2019 CO2 emissions: 108.7 million metric tonnes
5. Sinopec	2019 CO2 emissions: 116.2 million metric tonnes
6. Shell	2020 CO2 emissions: 70.6 million metric tonnes
7. China State Construction Engineering	2019 CO2 emissions: 6.4 million metric tonnes
8. Volkswagen	2020 CO2 emissions: 82.7 million metric tonnes
9. BP	2020 CO2 emissions: 55.4 million metric tonnes
10. Toyota	2020 CO2 emissions: 45.6 million metric tonnes

Figure 2: *Global carbon emissions of the top 10 companies in the world. Note that inconsistent reporting standards mean that what is included in some footprints is not included in others, making it difficult to compare these companies directly.*

A GLOBAL STANDARD FOR MEASURING GREENHOUSE GAS EMISSIONS

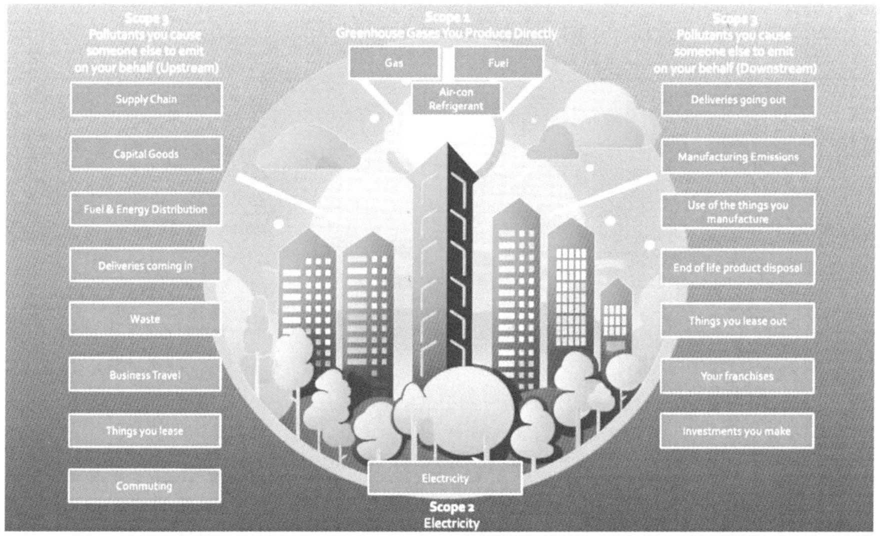

Figure 3: *Categorising carbon emissions.*

The Greenhouse Gas Protocol published by the World Resources Institute splits all carbon emissions into three basic groups:

- **Scope 1** - fuel you burn directly, which emits CO_2 directly. Typically, this is gas, diesel, and petrol.
- **Scope 2** - electricity, where CO_2 is emitted remotely by power generators, approximately in proportion to how much electricity you use.
- **Scope 3** - indirect emissions - in other words, emissions that you do not make yourself but that others emit on your behalf. For example, via products you buy, business travel, staff commuting, deliveries you make, and so on.

If you look closely at figure 3, you can see that emissions are also split broadly into two sections:

- **Upstream emissions** - emissions that are generated *before* you sell something, such as via the purchase of raw materials.
- **Downstream emissions** - everything emitted *after* you have sold something, such as via disposal of your product once it has reached the end of its useful life.

Scope 1 and Scope 2 are straightforward, but when we look at Scope 3, things can become more complicated. Emissions within Scope 3 are therefore further broken down into 15 different subdivisions to make them easier to work with, as shown in figure 4.

3.1 Purchased goods and services
3.2 Capital goods
3.3 Fuel- and energy-related activities (not included in Scope 1 or 2)
3.4 Upstream transportation and distribution
3.5 Waste generated in operations
3.6 Business travel
3.7 Employee commuting
3.8 Upstream leased assets
3.9 Downstream transportation and distribution
3.10 Processing of sold products
3.11 Use of sold products
3.12 End-of-life treatment of sold products
3.13 Downstream leased assets
3.14 Franchises
3.15 Investments

Figure 4: Scope 3 sub-divisions

NOT ALL SCOPE 3 CATEGORIES ARE BORN EQUAL

Scope 3 emissions can be horrendously complex to calculate. As an example, think about calculating the carbon footprint of a sales conference in Berlin when 314 people attend from all over the world. They stay in different sizes and classes of hotel and eat many different things from many different restaurants, with some eating only a local plant-based diet and others seeking out imported meats.

To simplify the problem of measuring emissions, we concentrate only on a sub-set of the Scope 3 categories which are both (a) the most relevant for the majority of businesses; and (b) required by the PPN 06/21 standard.

This is not to say that the Scope 3 factors we have decided to ignore are not important. But simplification of the problem to include only the six Scope

3 categories makes the process achievable, cost-effective and still fully compliant with PPN 06/21.

The six Scope 3 categories we concentrate on (in addition to all Scope 1 and Scope 2 emissions) are:

1. Supply Chain - what you buy
2. Deliveries coming in - the trucks, vans and cars carrying your deliveries
3. Deliveries you make to your customers - couriers, trucks, vans and so on
4. Business travel - planes, trains, hotels, taxis, and so on
5. Commuting - including the emissions of staff working from home
6. Waste

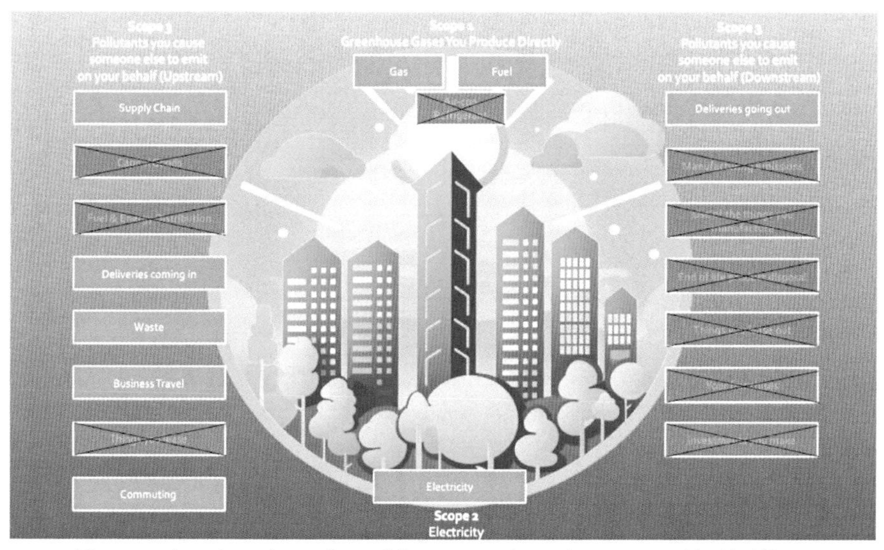

Figure 5: A reduced number of Scope 3 categories are used in Net Zero.

Note that this list, except for supply chain, is the same list defined in the PPN 06/21 standard, making all Net Zero Carbon Reduction Plans developed in line with these categories PPN 06/21 compliant.

WHAT DOES A TYPICAL CARBON FOOTPRINT LOOK LIKE?

Three popular carbon footprint statement reporting formats are shown in figure 6. The first shows the Net Zero layout and is our 'go to' layout, the second is a layout popular in the UK for financial reporting (as per the

Streamlined Energy and Carbon Reporting Regulation, or SECR) and the last is a report for a larger company showing a more detailed breakdown of their emissions.

The essential thing that all statements show is a breakdown of the major carbon categories that were analysed, along with some historic comparisons with previous years.

Category	Unit	2023	2022	Change (%)
Gas	tCO2e	1.3	1.6	-19%
Electricity	tCO2e	0.7	0.9	-22%
Transport	tCO2e	3.2	4.1	-22%
Supply chain	tCO2e	17.1	21.4	-20%
Deliveries in	tCO2e	0.2	0.2	0%
Deliveries out	tCO2e	0.3	0.3	0%
Business travel	tCO2e	6.4	7.9	-19%
Commuting & WFH	tCO2e	1.2	0.8	50%
Waste	tCO2e	0.1	0.1	0%
Total	tCO2e	30.5	37.3	-18%
Profit	£000	212	183	16%
Carbon Intensity	tCO2e/£1000	0.14	0.20	-29%
Certified Offsets		-30.5	-37.3	
Net carbon emissions	tCO2e	0	0	

Figure 6: An example Net Zero carbon footprint statement

	This reporting period (Jan 2021 - Dec 2021)	Prior reporting period (Jan 2020 - Dec 2020)
Total electricity use	2,181,885 kWh	2,463,876 kWh
Total gas use	1,882,253 kWh	1,480,147 kWh
Total transport fuel	959,953 kWh	379,760 k.Wh
Total energy from other fuels	0 kWh	0 kWh
Total energy use (all sources)	5,024,091 kWh	4,323,783 kWh

	This reporting period (Jan 2021 - Dec 2021)	Prior reporting period (Jan 2020 - Dec 2020)
Total carbon emissions (electricity)	636 tCO2e	718 tCO2e
Total carbon emissions (gas)	404 tCo2e	318 tCO2e
Total carbon emissions (transport fuel)	254 tCO 2e	112 tCO2e
Total carbon emissions (other sources)	otCO2e	otCO2e
Total carbon emissions	1,293 tCO2e	1,148 tCO2e
Total estate	253,423 sqft	253,423 sqft
Carbon intensity ratio	5.1 kgCo2e per sqft	4.53 kgCO2e per sqft
Carbon intensity ratio	10.62 kgCO2e per tonne of production	9.52 kgCO2e per tonne of production

Figure 7: An example SECR carbon footprint statement. Note the inclusion of kilowatt hours (kWh) in the table as well as carbon emissions

AMAZON'S ENTERPRISE-WIDE CARBON FOOTPRINT, 2019-2021

Carbon Intensity (grams of carbon dioxide equivalent per dollar of gross merchandise sales)	2019	2020	2021	YOY%
	122.8	102.7	100.8	-1.9%

Emission Category (million metric tonnes of carbon dioxide equivalent)	2019	2020	2021	YOY%
Emissions from Direct Operations (Scope 1)	5.76	9.62	12.11	26%
Fossil fuels	5.57	9.57	11.89	27%
Refrigerants	0.19	0.25	0.22	-12%
Emissions from Purchased Electricity (Scope 2)	5.50	5.27	4.07	-25%

Emission Category (million metric tonnes of carbon dioxide equivalent)	2019	2020	2021	YOY%
Emissions from Indirect Sources (Scope 3)	59.91	45.75	55.56	21 %
Corporate purchases and Amazon-branded product emissions (e.g., operating expenses, business travel, and Amazon-branded product manufacturing, use phase and end-of-life)	15.41	16.70	19.09	14%
Capital goods (e.g. building construction, servers and other hardware, equipment, vehicles)	8.01	10.52	15.57	46%
Other indirect emissions (e.g., third-party transport, packaging, upstream energy related)	12.44	15.77	18.00	14%
Life cycle emissions from customer trips to Amazon's physical stores	4.05	2.77	2.91	5%
Amazon's Total Footprint	**51.17**	**60.64**	**71.54**	**18%**

Figure 8: *Amazon's carbon footprint, totalling 71 million tCO2e. Source: Amazon*

With respect to comparisons with previous years, although it is useful to see these numbers, carbon footprint calculation methodologies do change frequently for Scope 3 emissions, and company sizes often change from year to year. Many suppliers currently only include Scope 1 and Scope 2 in their footprints, so you should expect their figures to increase significantly when they begin to include Scope 3. Absolute changes are therefore often less informative than you would expect, and carbon professionals would concentrate more on carbon intensities than absolute emissions. Further explanation on carbon intensities is given later in this book.

HOW TO USE CARBON FACTORS TO CALCULATE YOUR CARBON FOOTPRINT

To work out a carbon footprint of something, we first split it up into its constituent components. We then work out what the carbon emissions for each of those components are using pre-determined reference values, and add them up.

For example, for a trip from Oxford to Edinburgh, the carbon footprint can be defined in simple terms as:

The carbon footprint of the petrol used

+

The carbon footprint of things we bought along the way[2]

To work out the carbon emissions for each element of this equation, we use carbon factors. Carbon factors are conversion factors that have been calculated (generally by governments, but also trade groups or researchers) to convert an activity into an equivalent amount of carbon emissions. For example:

- Burning a litre of diesel emits 2.7kg of CO2, so 1 litre of diesel = 2.7 kgCO2e[3]
- 1 kilowatt hour (kWh) of electricity from the UK grid typically emits 0.193 kgCO2e[xii]
- Each chocolate bar we eat has associated emissions of 0.2 kgCO2e[xiii]

AN EXAMPLE FOOTPRINT CALCULATION OF A BUSINESS JOURNEY

Our trip from Oxford to Edinburgh was 367 miles and our car does 36 miles per gallon (mpg). As there are 4.55 litres per gallon, we can calculate the fuel used in litres as:

(367 / 36) x 4.55 litres = 46 litres of petrol

Referring to the conversion factors above, we will emit:

46 x 2.7 kgCO2e = 124 kgCO2e = 0.124 tCO2e

If we consumed a chocolate bar at both the Warwick services on the M42 and again at the Tebay services on the M6 (I know, I need to reduce my sugar intake, but it's a long journey), the chocolate bar emissions would add up to:

2 x 0.2 kgCO2e = 0.4 kgCO2e = 0.0004 tCO2e

Meaning that our trip from Oxford to Edinburgh would have a carbon factor of:

0.124 + 0.0004 tCO2e = 0.1244 tCO2e

2 We might also include the carbon emissions produced as a result of buying and maintaining the car, but for simplicity we will ignore this for now.

3 1 tCO2e = 1000 kgCO2e

When we look at calculating the carbon footprint of a business, we do the same exercise of splitting the business into its different component parts. For our purposes, we can define this as:

Our business carbon footprint = total carbon emissions from:

The electricity we use
+ the gas we burn
+ the fuel we put in our company vehicles
+ our business travel
+ our waste
+ what we buy
+ the delivery vans delivering to us
+ the delivery vans delivering things to our customers
+ staff coming to and from work
+ staff working from work

The carbon footprint of each of these components can be calculated by multiplying the size of each component – for example, the number of kilograms of waste generated – by a government factor that turns that component into carbon emissions, such as "waste (kg) -> carbon emissions (kgCO_2e)".

WHERE DO I FIND THESE CARBON FACTORS?

Carbon factors are calculated by a number of people, some with a higher degree of accuracy than others, but they are readily available on the internet by searching for "CO_2 emissions of a chocolate bar", or "average carbon emissions for a diesel car per mile". Make sure you are using a reputable source, such as the UK Government-approved figures[xiv]. If you are using software to calculate your carbon footprint, you will find these emissions are already built into the software kept up to date, which saves a significant amount of time. Note that most factors are updated annually, so make sure you are using the appropriate conversion factor for the correct year.

HOW TO CHOOSE FROM THE DIFFERENT TYPES OF CARBON FACTORS AVAILABLE

Six basic categories of factors exist, namely:

1. Rough estimates – for example, I bought an average amount of stationery for a company of my type, size and location
2. Industry average based – for example, I spent £500 with a stationery company

3. Supplier-based spending – for example, I bought £500 of products from Oxfordshire Office Supplies
4. Activity-based – for example, I bought 200 reams of A4 paper
5. Material-based – for example, I bought 600kg of grade 1 paper
6. Lifecycle assessment-based – for example, I bought 200 units of EPD reference code of Q51983

Some are more popular than others, some are simpler than others, some are more accurate than others and some are only applicable in certain cases.

Factor	Accuracy	Ease of use	Allowed in Certifi-cations	Notes
Rough estimates	*	*****	No	Extremely fast to use, but not very accurate
Industry average based	**	****	No	Quick and simple to use. Great for calculating quick, usable carbon footprints, but not accurate enough for certification
Supplier	**	**	Supply chain only	Not accurate enough for certification use on its own, except when used to calculate supply chain carbon
Activity	***	***	Yes	The preferred factor to use for certification along with supplier-based factors for supply chain analysis
Material	****	***	Yes	Used primarily in the manufacturing sector
Lifecycle assessment	*****	****	Yes	Used primarily in the construction sector

You should look at using the following factors as a rule of thumb:

1. 1. For 'quick and dirty' calculations to get you started, use estimates or industry average spends
2. 2. For a better picture, use supplier-based spend factors

3. 3. For certification, use activity-based factors as standard and supplier spend-based factors to calculate the emissions from your supply chain
4. 4. Manufacturers should do (3), but additionally use material-based factors to look at emissions from their raw material purchases
5. 5. Construction companies should do (3), but additionally use material-based factors for materials like cement and sand, and lifecycle assessment-based factors for components such as roof trusses
6. 6. Resellers should do (3), but also include the carbon footprint of the products resold using product-based factors *Rough estimates*[4]

Rough estimates are hugely inaccurate, but are good for getting up and running quickly. They cannot be used for certification purposes as they are simply not accurate enough.

An example rough estimate calculation might be:

> *Your school's carbon footprint =*
> *[the number of pupils in your school]*
> *x [the typical carbon footprint per pupil of a typical school in the UK]*

As you can see, in this example, everything rests on how 'typical' the school is compared to the norm. However, from experience, every school is different. For example, 'typical footprints per pupil' do not take into consideration the school building age or type, the heating systems and lighting used, the amount of travel to/from the school, and so on.

INDUSTRY AVERAGE-BASED

Sometimes called 'extended economic inputs and outputs' or 'EEIOs', these are a set of factors that governments produce to detail the average carbon emissions per pound spent in different industry sectors. For example:

> *Every £1 spend with accountants in the UK typically generates 0.02 kgCO2e.*

4 In reality, this is difficult as most products do not have lifecycle carbon footprint reference figures readily available. You could simplify it for now by looking solely at the total weight of all the products you buy split out into different types of material. However, most businesses simply flag this as a problem area that should be revisited in the future.

The factors are very broad and, because they average across a large and varied number of companies within each industry sector, they are very inaccurate.

To illustrate this, let's think about accountancy services. You might imagine that a very eco-conscious local accountant who works from home and meets only by video conference has a lower carbon footprint than a large London agency that flies its employees via business class to see clients and take them to swanky dinners. The carbon factors for these two businesses will be vastly different, yet they'll all be lumped together in one industry-average based factor called 'accountancy services'.

The factors used throughout most of the industry are reasonably old and require updating. Enistic also incorporates factors based on our own data sets, which have grown steadily over the years. This means that, in a lot of cases, our footprints are considerably more accurate than those calculated using only government figures.

SUPPLIER-BASED FACTORS

With supplier-based factors, you identify which specific supplier you used and what their specific carbon factor is, rather than using industry averages. As you might imagine, specifying the precise supplier will give you significantly more accurate estimates of the associated carbon emissions.

To calculate a specific supplier-based factor, take the carbon footprint of a specific supplier and divide this by their turnover. This should give you a figure for the carbon they emit per £ of turnover. For example, Oxfordshire Stationery Ltd has a turnover in 2021 of £235,000 and a carbon footprint of 17 tCO_2e. They therefore emit:

17 / 235000 tCO_2e per £1 of turnover *= 0.00007234 tCO_2e per £1 of turnover* *I.e. 0.00007234 tCO_2e/£*

To make this more readable, we can multiply by 1,000 to get $kgCO_2e$:

= 0.07234 $kgCO_2e$/£

If you a dealing with high turnovers, you can use $kgCO_2e$ per £1,000 or per $kgCO_2e$ per £1,000,000 by multiplying accordingly. In our case, we could write our emissions intensity as:

= 72.34 $kgCO_2e$/£000

Therefore, imagine if we spent £17,500 with them in 2021, we would have caused emissions of:

17.5 x 72.34 tCO2e = 1,270 kgCO2e = 1.3 tCO2e

This would be the figure we put into our carbon calculations.

Top tip

As we have seen, to make the numbers more manageable, some companies quote tCO2e per £1,000, or kgCO2e per £1,000.

They are all equivalent values, just in different units. Be careful, therefore, to double-check the exact units being used.

ACTIVITY-BASED FACTORS

The next class of carbon factor is activity-based factors. These are the most popular factors used in the industry today and are usually the factors used for Net Zero calculations.

Activity-based factors are a series of factors that say:

If you do this activity, you will emit X kgCO2e

For example, in the UK, an activity-based factor for passenger train travel is:

Each 1km of passenger train travel on National Rail emits 0.03549 kgCO2e

So, if we went from Edinburgh from London by train, which is 534km, the journey would emit:

534km x 0.03549 kgCO2e = 18.95 kgCO2e = 0.019 tCO2e

Notice that, unlike the previously mentioned factors, activity-based factors are not based on what you spend, but an absolute measure of what you do. In other words, the 'activity' above is the act of one person travelling 1km on a train, whereas previously it was one person spending £1 as a result of travelling by train.

As another example: for each kilogram of general waste that is produced, 21.3 kgCO2e of emissions will typically be generated. Enistic sent 31 tonnes of waste to be incinerated last year, so the associated emissions were:

31 x 1000 kg x 21.3 kgCO2e / tonne = 660,000 kgCO2e = 660 tCO2e

Activity-based factors are significantly more accurate than spend-based factors and their use is very common. They are the accepted norm for certifiable carbon footprint calculations for everything except (a) supply-chain calculations (which are typically performed using supplier-based factors); and (b) specific material and lifecycle analysis calculations for manufacturing and construction companies.

MATERIAL-BASED FACTORS

These are factors which measure carbon emissions per unit of material consumed which is called the "Embodied Carbon Emissions" of a material, generally shortened to either "Embodied Carbon" or "Embodied Emissions". They include all emissions associated with its sourcing and production. For example:

1 tonne of aluminium used causes emissions of 4.8 tCO2e[xv]

Material-based factors are only useful for manufacturers to calculate part of their total emissions. To calculate the total emissions, you have to use these factors for the Embodied Carbon component and then add the Operational Emissions which are the emissions from all the other more usual operations, such as travel, light, heat etc. In simple terms:

Total Carbon Footprint = Embodied Carbon + Operational Emissions

If you take this approach, you will end up stating two emissions numbers, one for each component of your carbon footprint. As your Embodied Carbon is generally significantly larger than your Operational Emissions, splitting them out and reporting on them separately allows you to track the benefit of your carbon reduction projects without them being lost in the much larger, overall figure.

These factors will generally be built into the software platform you are using but are also widely available online.

Reporting emissions from a plastic bottle manufacturer

Lee has a small factory that makes 50ml plastic bottles which are sold into the cosmetics trade. He buys 30 tonnes of LDPE plastic pellets each month, has 3 company cars that his sales reps use and uses a typical blend of electricity and gas to run his factory.

He chooses to report the emissions of his plastic purchases separately from the rest of his emissions as he has less control over the carbon emissions associated with the production of the plastic than he does over the running of his factory and the associated vehicle use.

His Operational Emissions were calculated in the normal way as 3.1 tCO2e per month.

His carbon footprint each month is:

[Embodied Carbon] + [Operational Emissions]

= 30 x [Material-based carbon factor for LDPE] + 3.1

= 30 x 2.08 + 3.1 tCO2e = 62.4 + 3.1 tCO2e = 65.5 tCO2e

He reports his carbon emissions as follows:

Our Total Emissions last month were 65.5 tCO2e which was comprised of 3.1 tCO2e of Operational Emissions and 62.4 tCO2e of Embodied Carbon in our raw materials.

LIFECYCLE ANALYSIS-BASED FACTORS

Lifecycle analysis-based factors (LCAs) are the most accurate factors available for product purchases and are very common in the construction industry.

They refer to specific products manufactured by a specific manufacturer during a specific period. For example:

Each '15cmx15cm Aletha Ceramic Flooring Tile with Floral Print' (item code FTA1503) which was manufactured between 2019 and 2021 by Sepia Floor Tiles Ltd (company number 8130912) in Nottingham-On-Trent has associated emissions of 0.713 kgCO2e per tile

If you are building a house with 290 of these tiles, the total carbon emissions for that would be:

290 tiles x 0.713 kgCO2e = 206.77 kgCO2e = 0.2 tCO2e

To calculate an LCA factor, a researcher will look at the entire carbon footprint of a specific product in detail, from cradle to grave. They examine what materials it is made from, the carbon each material contains, where it came from, how it was transported from its source to the factory, what emissions were made during manufacturing, what emissions were involved with transporting it, and what emissions there will be when the product has reached the end of its life and is scrapped.

LCA calculations are relatively complex and can take months of work to calculate. The result is (normally) a very accurate estimate of the carbon content of a product. Once calculated, manufacturers can send their analysis for third-party accreditation. If approved, they can be wrapped up into a document called an environmental product declaration (EPD - an officially approved LCA calculation carried out according to specific standards), given a reference number, and added to one of several large databases of such documents for architects or other professionals to access.

As with materials-based factors, if you have a significant amount of Lifecycle analysis-based emissions you should report them separately. This is especially true for companies in the construction industry where dual reporting like this is commonplace.

Reporting emissions from a house builder

Jake is a residential housing developer, typically developing 3 - 4 projects at any one time, with an average of 6 - 10 houses per project.

He uses EPDs to calculate the Embodied Carbon of the components he uses to construct each house such as window frames, door frames, roof trusses etc, although he has had to estimate significantly in many cases as his suppliers could not always supply an EPD. He uses material-based factors to calculate the Embodied Carbon of cement, concrete and paint. He adds these emissions to the EPD derived emissions to give him his total Embodied Carbon Emissions.

He chooses to report the Embedded Carbon separately from the rest of his emissions as he has less control over the carbon emissions associated with the products and materials he buys in. This allows to both focus on reducing the carbon emissions of each house he builds whilst at the same time becoming a more sustainable business himself.

He reports his carbon as follows:

Our Total Emissions last year were 4,218 tCO2e. This was comprised of 178 tCO2e of Operational Emissions and 4,040 tCO2e of Embodied Carbon in the materials and products used.

We completed construction of 28 units with an average of 150 tCO2e per unit.

The completed units had a combined gross area of 3,112 m2 meaning we had an emissions intensity of 1.4 tCO2e per m2.

HOW ACCURATE ARE CARBON FACTORS?

Broadly speaking, the more detail you go into about your specific circumstances, the more accurate carbon factors will be. For example, an industry-based cost analysis of

£6,000 worth of building materials

is not as accurate as a supplier-based analysis of

£6,000 *worth of materials from supplier X*

Which, in turn, is not as accurate as a lifecycle-based analysis:

6 pieces of 'A31-B' roof truss with EPD reference number Q98143 *and* *300 pieces of 'EasyClay-37G' roof tiles with EPD number Q182133*

The more accurate you can be in specifying what it is you do or what you buy, the more detailed carbon factor you can use, which gives you a more accurate result. It is important, however, to remember these are all estimates and are never 100% accurate.

WHICH FACTORS SHOULD I CHOOSE?

It is usually sufficient to use the factors built into the software you choose to calculate your carbon footprint, as there will generally have been a great deal of time and effort put into selecting them, where to source them from and which version of them to use. Nevertheless, as a rule of thumb:

- Use rough estimates for the Net Zero catapult, as these are quick and easy to use and they give you an early reward for your efforts
- Use industry-average factors for small companies where there is not much time available for calculating carbon footprints
- Use a mix of activity-based and supplier-based factors for everything else, especially if you want certification for your footprint

The only exceptions are manufacturing and construction. In these industries, it is important to think carefully about which factors will deliver the most appropriate accuracy for the time you have available, or for what your customer has asked for. In many cases, the EPD, lifecycle-based or material-based factors are becoming integrated into the Computer Aided Design or Building Information Management systems in a way that would enable you to simply export a carbon report at the end of the design process.

You can also blend different factors together if needed. For example, manufacturers could use material-based factors for their raw materials, activity-based factors for the energy they use and supplier-based factors for things they buy other than raw materials. Simply select the most appropriate factor for your circumstances and swap between the different types of factor as you see fit.

Top tip

If you use different types of factors to calculate your carbon footprint, be careful not to double-count things.

For example, in a supplier-based analysis of your supply chain purchases, make sure you do not include your British Airways spend if you already have those flights detailed in the business travel section of your analysis.

An easy mistake in this area is double-counting electric vehicles that have already been accounted for as they were charged on site, so are already included in the site electricity use.

TOOLS OF THE TRADE

If the idea of wading through pages and pages of factors and finding the right ones seems off-putting you may only want to consider your Scope 1 and 2 footprints (electricity, gas and fuel). It is relatively easy to set up a simple spreadsheet to calculate Scope 1 and Scope 2 emissions, but for anything meaningful, especially for Scope 3, you should use software to do the work for you.

For example, using longitude and latitude coordinates, it is possible to calculate the flying distance between airport A and airport B. You can then multiply that by the appropriate carbon factor for business, economy or first-class air travel, or you could simply type the names of the airports and let the software do it for you.

At Enistic, we provide such software at an affordable price, to make it easy for businesses to get involved. It is also entirely free for academic use[xvi].

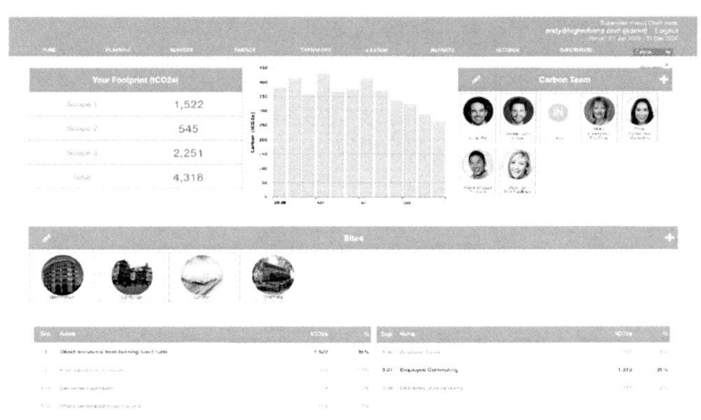

Figure 9: The Enistic carbon management platform

10

WHAT IS A CARBON REDUCTION PLAN?

A Carbon Reduction Plan is a document that explains how your business will achieve Net Zero. They come in all different shapes and sizes - some are short, some are long, and some are highly polished, well-designed pieces of art whilst others are simple pages of A4 text. They all, however, have one thing in common: they contain the critical MARTOC components, without which they would be incomplete and fail certification.

Top tip

Many companies make the mistake of having one Carbon Reduction Plan for their entire organisation, instead of having one plan per site which are then consolidated at a group level for reporting purposes.

This may mean that the plan is not directly relevant to all the sites included in the report, some of which may have distinct characteristics, such as being in a remote location, having assembly operations on site, or being particularly large or small etc.

To make the plans relevant, ensure that you have one Carbon Reduction Plan per site.

A typical Carbon Reduction Plan might contain the following information:

- Section 1 - A cover page clearly stating that this a Carbon Reduction Plan compliant with PPN 06/21, the company name and date range it covers
- Section 2 - A statement, typically from a senior representative in your organisation such as a director or CEO, explaining your carbon strategy. This should cover headline themes and topics you would like to focus on as a business, for example the elimination of all single use plastics in your packaging
- Section 3 - **M**easurement of your carbon footprint - what you carbon footprint is, broken down according to Scopes 1, 2 and 3 (see page ?), alongside commentary on the figures and historic comparisons against previous years
- Section 4 - **A**im to reduce your emissions by X% in a given time period - for example, "a 45% reduction in all emissions by 2030"
- Section 5 - **R**educe - your Carbon Reduction Plans. This should include detail of the actions you will take, the emissions you aim to save and the time frame, as well as discussion of the potential challenges.

- Section 6 - **T**rack your progress over recent years and provide commentary on the figures. This section normally has a chart showing actual emissions versus planned emissions.
- Section 7 - **O**ffsets and removals - what you are doing to offset and/ or remove the emissions you continue to generate.
- Section 8 - **C**ertify and commit - including accreditation from a third party and a written commitment from a senior director within the company.

MAKE YOUR PLAN STAND OUT FROM THE CROWD

There are a couple of things you can do to help your Carbon Reduction Plan stand out amongst the competition.

First, make sure your plan is clear and concise and does not contain too much trade-specific jargon. Second, spend some time on the design of the plan: put a nice cover on it, include some relevant images, and make sure graphs are understandable and appealing and that they're correctly formatted, etc.

Top tip

Not everybody is going to read every word you write in your Carbon Reduction Plan. To help those who want the important information upfront, think about including an infographic at the beginning of the document. Something that showcases the key elements of the plan, arranged in a visually appealing way.

So you'll look at putting the key data in, such as what's your footprint, what are the plans

Finally, consider the transparency and honesty of the report. If you have had to, for example, estimate emissions generated by business travel, make this clear. It's okay to say, "*We don't have the flight information from earlier in the year*", as long as you explain what you are going to do about it for next year's report.

THREE PHASES OF YOUR NET ZERO JOURNEY

In theory, all you must do to write a great Carbon Reduction Plan is apply the MARTOC method. However, there are two other aspects we need to consider: (a) the problems associated with initially getting the data you need, which can lead to a prolonged delay before your first plan is available; and (b) the necessity of repeating the process annually.

To help with these problems, we introduce a phased approach to completing your plan:

1. **Phase 1 - The Net Zero catapult** - to get you up and running fast. This is described in further detail in Chapter 4.
2. **Phase 2 – The MARTOC method** – structure your Carbon Reduction Plan according to the process described in Chapters 6 - 12.
3. **Phase 3 – Maintenance** – Carbon Reduction Plans are typically published annually, so it is necessary to repeat the process each year. This is described in more detail in the Chapter 10.

PHASE 1: THE NET ZERO CATAPULT

The Net Zero catapult is designed to make it easier to get started on your Carbon Reduction Plan when you may have a shortage of data on your emissions. It involves making an initial assessment based upon assumptions.

For example, instead of asking for all the data relating to flights taken in the past year, including the origin, destination and class of each flight, we ask *"Roughly, how many short-haul flights were taken this year?"* This is a much simpler question to answer and allows us to begin to get a handle on the size and shape of a carbon footprint extremely quickly. As more data then becomes available, initial estimates can be replaced with more accurate figures.

Top tip

In the real world, if your manager has asked you to prepare a Carbon Reduction Plan for the company, the Net Zero catapult is a great way of getting something into their hands fast.

Some Carbon Reduction Plan projects can take a long time because of the problems associated with getting all the data required. So, to get a quick win like this can get you some much deserved, shorter-term praise from your superiors.

PHASE 2 – THE MARTOC METHOD

Now you have some idea of your carbon footprint and where the difficult areas to obtain data might be, you can use the MARTOC method to fill in the bulk of your first 'proper' (i.e. non-catapult) Carbon Reduction Plan. As you will remember, MARTOC includes the components Measure, Aim, Reduce, Track, Offset and Certify. Each of these is covered in more depth later in this book.

PHASE 3 – MAINTENANCE

Carbon Reduction Plans are updated and re-published annually. Preparing your first plan always takes longer than subsequent plans, and there are some tricks and tips later in this book about how to make the process easier when it is repeated.

FREQUENTLY ASKED QUESTIONS

Before we start looking at each of the MARTOC sections in detail, here are some answers to the questions I get asked frequently.

1) WHAT ARE THE MAIN BUSINESS BENEFITS OF ACHIEVING NET ZERO?

Broadly speaking, becoming a more sustainable company engenders a more caring, inclusive and modern work environment, which is appealing to new talent. This can ultimately lead to a lower staff turnover rate, lower recruitment costs and improved company culture.

As suppliers are increasingly asking for sustainability credentials when awarding contracts, it can also lead to a more profitable company that wins more tenders and attracts better clients.

2) HOW LONG DOES IT TAKE TO CREATE A CARBON REDUCTION PLAN?

Using the Net Zero catapult, you can get your first (very rough) Carbon Reduction Plan quite easily in an afternoon. With some basic details about your company, you can go through the catapult process and get an outline plan in one sitting using online software.

The refinement process begins the minute you finish the catapult. In my experience, you are likely to get most of your data input in weeks one and two, with a view to finishing off the process in weeks three to four. As such, broadly speaking, you should allow four weeks from get-go to having a Carbon Reduction Plan you can be proud of.

3) WILL I GET CERTIFIED AT THE END OF THE PROCESS?

If you produce a coherent Carbon Reduction Plan including all of the MARTOC components, you should receive certification if you apply with an official body.

If you choose to produce a Carbon Reduction Plan but decide that offsetting and/or removal of CO_2 is too expensive, then you are still doing better than most companies by at least having a plan. However, you will not be able to be certified.

4) WHO CERTIFIES ME?

You can use a certification company, or you can self-certify.

As certification is new, there are not many companies that currently offer it[5], but I expect there will be an increasing number as time goes on. There are no firm regulations about who can and cannot certify you to the Net Zero standards set out in this book, so there's nothing stopping you from self-certifying. However, this may be frowned upon by your clients and other stakeholders, and by self-certifying you miss out on the benefits that having a third-party check your work can bring.

Remember that certification is an annual process with each certificate lasting 12 months.

5) DO I NEED TO REDUCE MY CARBON EMISSIONS? CAN'T I JUST BUY CARBON OFFSETS?

If you want to become certified, you need to both buy offsets/removals *and* reduce your carbon emissions to the lowest level you practically can.

5 In another shameless plug, Enistic has been offering certification services since 2014

6) HOW MUCH DOES ACHIEVING NET ZERO COST?

There are four costs to consider:

1. Internal management time needed for collecting and inputting data into the software platform. Cost: This is an internal cost and typically absorbed into people's general workloads.
2. Software and certification costs. Cost: Typically, certification costs approximately £95 per annum for a small company, though for larger companies it can be significantly more. Carbon Reduction Plan software is typically less than £40 per month.
3. Costs associated with carrying out the reduction projects you identified during the process (though these can be done over the course of a few years and, typically, save energy and hence costs at the same time). Cost: This varies hugely and is impossible to generalise. For example, a new heat-pump installation costs significantly more than installing LED lighting.
4. Costs associated with offsetting or removing your carbon emissions. Costs: At the time of writing, offsets cost approximately £35 per tonne, though you can get poorer quality schemes for as little as £7 per tonne and high-end projects can cost over £60 per tonne. Removals currently cost upwards of £1,200 per tonne, though governments have indicated that the longer-term price target will be close to £220 per tonne.

7) HOW ACCURATE ARE CARBON FOOTPRINTS?

They vary hugely, but if you follow the MARTOC stages laid out in this book and use actual monthly data rather than estimated data, the carbon footprints produced are considered accurate enough for day-to-day use. That's not to say they could not be more accurate, but the levels set out in this book represent what is considered an acceptable balance between accuracy and preparation workload.

Note that the Net Zero catapult is known to be reasonably inaccurate, but is designed to get you up and running quickly with a view to refining later in the process.

8) CAN I USE MY NET ZERO CERTIFICATE WITH MY CUSTOMERS?

You absolutely can, and the more customers you show your credentials to, the better. As certified Net Zero meets and exceeds the requirements of PPN 06/21, if you are ever asked for it you can use your certificate as proof of compliance. This is one of the intended uses of the Net Zero certificate. It's designed for you as a business to say proudly:

> *"We care about our environmental impact. We've thought about it, we've got a plan in place to reduce it, we're involving as many people as we can in the plan, and here's a certificate to say someone else has looked through it and agrees that it meets the required quality standards."*

9) I WORK FOR A LARGE BUSINESS. CAN I USE MY CARBON REDUCTION PLAN TO MEET MY LEGAL OBLIGATIONS?

It really depends on which requirement you are referring to. For example:

1. The Streamlined Energy and Carbon Reporting legislation (SECR): Yes, you can, but it will need slight reformatting before it is acceptable.
2. The Energy Saving Opportunities Scheme (ESOS): Partly yes, but you will have to do additional onsite energy audits and data reporting to become fully compliant. Your Carbon Reduction Plan, however, will account for the bulk of the work you need to do.
3. Procurement Policy Notice 06/21 (PPN 06/21): Yes, you can.
4. The Taskforce on Climate-Related Financial Disclosures (TCFD): No, you need to carry out considerably more work to extend what you have done in your Carbon Reduction Plan, but the work you have done will be required, so it is not wasted effort.
5. Science Based Targets: No, the same applies as for the TCFD.
6. Environmental, social and governance (ESG) reporting: The Carbon Reduction Plan forms the core of ESG reporting, but there are other sections you will need to add.
7. BCorp Certification: Yes, but you will need to add a significant number of additional items to meet the full standard.

10) WHAT HAPPENS IF I HAVE MULTIPLE SITES?

You should produce one Carbon Reduction Plan for each site and a consolidated plan that pulls everything together for centralised reporting and analysis at board level.

The individual plans help to keep the data and recommendations as close to the people who can influence them as possible. This allows them to see improvements in their own carbon footprints as they make changes, and the effort they put in is not lost in a massive, centralised report.

If your sites are similar in nature, you may consider setting up league tables of sites to show which are performing the best and reward staff accordingly if they show improvements in their position in the league table.

11) CAN I IGNORE SOME SITES WHEN CALCULATING MY CARBON FOOTPRINT?

Some companies have small offices that operate solely out of shared facilities or are leased on all-inclusive basis. Generally, if you can answer 'no' to the following questions, you can leave that site out of your Carbon Reduction Plan:

1. Do you get a separate bill for the electricity or gas showing precisely how much energy you use to power the site?
2. Do you specify what lights to use on the site and/or when the lights break, do you fix them?
3. Did you specify what heating and/or cooling system was installed on the site, and if it breaks, are you responsible for fixing it?
4. Are you the largest tenant in the building?[6]

12) SHOULD I USE MY TAX YEAR OR THE CALENDAR YEAR TO WORK OUT MY CARBON FOOTPRINT?

It doesn't really matter which you choose, so long as you are consistent year-on-year. However, most people use their tax year as it ties in nicely with their annual accounts.

6 As the largest tenant in the building, you should have a degree of influence over the landlord to change aspects of the equipment used in the building.

“Climate change is one of the most difficult challenges the world has ever taken on, But I believe we can avoid a climate catastrophe if we take steps now to reduce emissions and find ways to adapt to a warmer world.”

Bill gates, 2020

Chapter 3

PREPARING FOR YOUR NET ZERO JOURNEY

By now, you should understand that net zero is not really a destination – rather, it's a journey, and a way of bringing sustainability into the core of your business. This chapter explores what you should do before setting off on this journey, to ensure the process runs as smoothly as possible when you come to start working on the plan in earnest.

Let's start with adopting a useful carbon strategy which sets out your company's approach towards carbon emissions. For example:

- Are you just going to ignore your emissions?
- Are you going to reduce your emissions?
- Are you going to reduce them a lot or a little?
- Are you going to be a sector leader in sustainability?

The carbon strategy crystalises this decision and sets the scene for all the work you're going to do in this area. It's normally quite short, with a typical carbon strategy running perhaps to one or two paragraphs, normally be drawn up by the project manager and then signed off by the board of directors.

WHY SHOULD YOU ADOPT A CARBON STRATEGY?

Having a carbon strategy establishes the overall direction of your carbon reduction journey and gives you some boundaries to your carbon reduction plan. It sets the scene for your forthcoming work and forms the backdrop of the plans you develop. In theory, you know that there will be support at board level for doing what you set out to do because everyone, even the board, has agreed on the objective.

Ideally, this also means you will get the resources you need for your plans, although we all recognise that plans change as circumstances change. The idea that you can ask for any project and have it approved is probably a bit far-fetched, but at least for most projects you can say:

> *"We agreed that the company would become sector leaders in sustainability by 2025. This is what we need to do to achieve this."*

SOME POPULAR CARBON STRATEGIES TO CHOOSE FROM

LEVEL 1 - NO STRATEGY

The first level is no carbon strategy at all. Nothing is written down, nothing is formally defined, and emission levels are probably not even regularly discussed. Hopefully, if you are in this category, you won't be for much longer.

LEVEL 2 - BASIC COMPLIANCE

The next level up is basic compliance, or minimal legal compliance. These carbon strategies, sadly, are far more popular than they should be. They are for companies that say:

> *"We intend to stay within the letter of the law. If the law requires us to do a report on environmental aspect A or B, we will do exactly that, but no more."*

No one's going to act on it, and probably no one is even going to read it."

The number of companies that do this is far too large. In 2015, approximately 90% of the companies I dealt with fit into this category. The only reason they had a strategy was because they had to, and they certainly didn't intend to either read the Carbon Reduction Plans we gave them or do anything about lowering their emissions.

When we look four years later in 2019, the situation had improved and somewhere between 50-60% of the companies that we dealt with were looking to do minimal compliance.

I'm pleased to say that, fast forward another four years to 2023, and the situation is significantly better. Whether that's because of increasing pressure from customers requiring their suppliers to be more sustainable, or whether it's the soaring energy costs, I don't know. Nevertheless, there is undoubtedly more interest in carbon reduction, and I would estimate that only 20-30% of the companies I deal with have no real interest in reducing their emissions.

LEVEL 3 – BEYOND COMPLIANCE FOR COMMERCIAL GAIN ('GREENWASHING')

You could broadly describe Level 3 as:

> *"We have been asked by our suppliers to go beyond the basic legal minimum because if we don't, we're not going to win this new contract. We don't really care, but we need to look green."*

To paraphrase this level, it is companies saying very publicly:

> *"We really care about the environment. We really, really, really do. Promise."*

However, at this level, companies tend to be doing no more than the minimum they can get away with. They have no plan and have certainly not considered the MARTOC method, but they say they are sustainable. Companies like this are deliberately misleading at worst – for example, purchasing one electric vehicle in a fleet of petrol burners and claiming to be sustainable.

LEVEL 4 – CERTIFIED NET ZERO

At Level 4, companies have reached the point where they are able to say:

> *"We care about the environment. We follow a recognised standard and will publish our Carbon Reduction Plans and put measures in place to transparently transition our company from where it is now to a more sustainable position."*

All certified Net Zero companies should be at this level. Thinking, planning and transparently executing practical solutions to achieve a more sustainable basis on which to do business.

An example Level 4 carbon strategy message

We passionately believe in reducing our carbon footprint and doing our part to protect the planet. We intend to become certified Net Zero by 2027.

We recognise that we are only at the start of this journey, but we are making every effort within our business to reduce carbon emissions in a thought-through and structured fashion.

[Sarah Jones], a senior director of the company, has taken responsibility to coordinate our sustainability efforts. She has personally ratified our Carbon Reduction Plan, which has been published on our website and received third-party certification from [Enistic].

In the plan, we explain how we intend to achieve Net Zero and show our progress to date. We'd appreciate any feedback you may have on how the plan could be improved, or how we could do more to operate in a more sustainable way.

LEVEL 5 – BEST IN CLASS

Level 5, best in class, is something I see amongst 5-10% of my clients. They are able to say:

> *"We are going to be the most sustainable company in our sector, and act as an example to others about what can be achieved. We want to be seen as leaders in this field. We're going to publish our plans and our progress transparently for all to see, and if you have any ideas how we could improve even further, please feel free to let us know."*

Level 5 is the highest level of carbon policy. I typically see it adopted by companies whose reputation and brand are of paramount importance to them. Coincidentally, these are often companies that have been in existence for a long time and/or where board members have a strong sense of ethics.

Which carbon strategy should I choose?

In terms of which to choose for your company, if it's Level 1, 2 or 3 then I suggest you stop reading this book. You should be choosing either Level 4 or Level 5, with Level 4 being a good happy medium for practical, day-to-day use and Level 5 being suitable for businesses that are particularly proud of their brand and have the resources available to lead from the front.

The carbon reduction dream team

If you are looking at producing a Net Zero plan on your own, it's not impossible. However, involving more people will not only make your job easier, it will also lead to increased engagement across the company. Net Zero should not be about one person sitting in a corner screaming "We should be green!"; it should be about trying to change the culture within your company to achieve a more sustainable way of thinking and working.

Who should you have on your carbon reduction dream team?

Firstly, you will need a project manager, perhaps yourself. If you're reading this, maybe you're the type of person who can motivate the team, organise meetings and check up on progress. You will certainly need a project manager; you can't do without one.

You should also include someone from your finance department. A significant amount of the data you required to achieve Net Zero is going to be supplied by the finance department. They know how much you spend on paper, how much you spend with each supplier, what the mileage reclaims for staff are, how much you spend on business travel, and so on.

You may need people from the facilities team, or the office manager if you have one. They can be a very important part of the carbon team, as often they understand the most about what's happening on site and can ensure the plans you make are grounded in the real world. As we discussed before, you should aim at producing one Carbon Reduction Plan per site, so if you have multiple sites you should recruit the facilities manager on each to work on their own, independent plan.

Finally, if you are involved in any form of manufacturing, look at involving the production manager or head of engineering, as they know about your industrial processes. They can help find and implement energy and carbon reduction projects in their areas.

Green champions and green teams

The other obvious people to include in your carbon reduction dream team are your colleagues. If you're a small company, form a small working group of three or four people and meet once a month to go through how projects are progressing and what can be done to reduce emissions.

Larger companies should consider a system of volunteer 'green champions'. Most businesses will have people in them that are willing to help given the right encouragement, and they can be instrumental in spreading the word of what you are trying to do and provide useful feedback to the carbon Team.

If you can, try not to be a one-person army, and try to get as many people involved as you can. The last thing you want is to be the developer of a Carbon Reduction Plan that no-one reads, and the sooner you can get others involved in the journey, the better.

What data do I need for Net Zero?

There are two answers to this: first, the data you will need for the Net Zero catapult; and subsequently, that needed for the Carbon Reduction Plan itself.

If you're doing the catapult, then all you really need is a general understanding of what is happening in your business. The catapult is not designed to be an exhaustive process, but is rather intended to get you from nothing to something with only a minimal amount of data in as short a time as possible. You need to know broadly how many flights were taken, how many nights were stayed in hotels, how many business journeys were taken, what kind of deliveries you've got, and so on. Rough estimates in the catapult are fine, and are in fact what most people use. It is only when you come to do the full Carbon Reduction Plan that you're going to require accurate monthly data.

Much of the data needed for the Carbon Reduction Plan is unlikely to be available to you from day one. More realistically, you'll have some of the data you need but not all, and you must plan on how to get hold of it on a regular basis going forward.

When considering your Net Zero data, think about:

1. What data do I need?
2. How frequently do I need it?
3. What level of accuracy does it need to have?
4. What format does it need to be in?
5. Who can provide all of this to me on a regular basis?

For much of the data you require, it might mean writing a couple of new reports that your central systems can output. For other data items, it may mean asking individuals to start regularly (typically monthly) entering their data into your Carbon Reduction Plan software so you have access to it. In my experience, if they are busy, there may be some initial reluctance, but once the process starts running smoothly, you will have what you need to do the job.

Note that there are bound to be gaps in the data, so if find some, don't worry. With each data gap, make a note of it and consider how you can rectify the situation for next time. These notes should be put into the 'track and revise' section of your plan.

The data required for a Net Zero catapult roughly includes:

1. How large your building is, or how many beds, rooms, or students it has (whichever is relevant to your business)
2. How many domestic, short-haul, and long-haul flights your employees take each year
3. How many deliveries you receive each week, and whether they are by courier, van or lorry
4. How many deliveries you make each week by courier, van or lorry
5. What you spend on electricity and gas each year
6. How many company vehicles you have and whether they do roughly more or less than an average number of miles per year
7. How many people commute into work, and whether they travel roughly an average, more than average or less than average distance
8. Whether you produce an average, more than average or less than average amount of waste

Note that this list is simplistic in nature, which is deliberate. The Net Zero catapult is designed to be quick to complete and rough estimates are precisely what is needed at this stage.

For the Carbon Reduction Plan, you will need data for the following items, ideally monthly, though annual data is acceptable if monthly data is not available:

Business travel:

1. The amount of fuel purchased for company vehicles
2. The number of miles your staff travelled on company business that they claimed back on expenses
3. The number of flights taken and their origin, destination and class of flight
4. The number of nights stayed in hotels and where those hotels were
5. The number of train miles travelled

Waste:

1. How many kilograms of waste you generated and what happened to that waste

Commuting:

1. How many staff commuted, what mode of transport they used and how far they travelled. This is easily collected via a staff questionnaire
2. How often staff worked from home
3. Your electricity, gas, and heating fuel use
4. How many deliveries you made and received, how far were they on average and whether you used a courier, van or a lorry
5. What you purchased each month - this is normally an export of your accounting system's purchase ledger

Figure 10: The data input categories needed for Net Zero are shown in the left-hand menu in this screenshot of the Yeti program.

TOP TIPS TO HELP MAKE YOUR NET ZERO PROJECT RUN SMOOTHLY

The Net Zero process is reasonably straightforward, but sometimes trips up. Here are my top three tips on how to help the project run more smoothly.

1. Enlist the support of a friendly company director

- Hint at the problems you're having with clients asking for your green credentials: *"Client X wants to see our Carbon Reduction Plan, it's a pity we don't have one..."*
- Where possible, find examples of pushback during your recruitment processes. Gen-Z, specifically, are extremely keen to work for ethical

companies and are likely to vote with their feet when it comes to working for a non-sustainably aware company.

- If you find staff are leaving the business, during exit interviews some may have mentioned either your company's lack of green credentials, or that they went to work for a company with a better environmental stance.
- If the director you are trying to court understands that sustainability issues are affecting their own bottom line and not just the planet, maybe they will be more receptive to change.

Top tip: Selling Net Zero to senior management.

You could consider presenting the Carbon Reduction Plan to senior managers as a set of three-year annual milestones and objectives. In my experience senior management love this. They like having absolute things they can point to, measure, compare, and tick off far more than gradual changes in culture and attitude.

In a similar vein, an effective way of getting buy-in is to include some measurable stats surrounding the aspects that you think will be impacted by the Net Zero process, such as staff retention, the company's ability to attract talent, improved brand image, lowered operational costs and increased percentage of won contracts. If you can do this, you are going to get more senior managers who want to help you, because they better understand the benefits of what you are doing.

2. Communicate to win

When you start the project, reach out and tell as many people as you possibly can what you're trying to do and why. Tell them what benefits they're going to get at the end of it, the shape of the journey you are all going to be on, how long it is likely to take, and if you need any help from them. As you progress, consider providing a regular Net Zero update and emphasise what you have achieved, where you have hit problems, what's gone particularly well, what customers, suppliers, and stakeholders are saying, and finally how people can get involved.

Try to make your updates easy to understand. Not everybody understands what a tonne of CO2 looks like, and not everyone wants to know what a tonne of CO2 looks like. Think about how you can communicate your message to people in a language they can understand, perhaps with simple graphics showing a before and after picture and some future targets.

Finally, when you are successful, shout it from the rooftops. If you won a contract partly because you had an impressive Carbon Reduction Plan in place, share the achievement with your colleagues.

3. Regular management meetings and board attention

Assuming you have formed your carbon reduction dream team, think about setting up regular meetings in everyone's diary to check on progress and sort out any difficulties that may arise. Typically, these should be held monthly.

Less frequently - for example, quarterly - you could include a repeating board agenda item to monitor your Net Zero progress. In most instances this could simply be, "Yes, everything's going fine". But if you have the board's attention once per quarter, you know that you will have the opportunity to raise any concerns should they arise.

"We need scientists to design new fuels. We need farmers to help grow them. We need engineers to invent new technologies. We need entrepreneurs to sell those technologies. We need workers to operate assembly lines that hum with high-tech, zero-carbon components. We need builders to hammer into place the foundations for a clean energy age. We need diplomats and businessmen and women, and Peace Corps volunteers to help developing nations skip past the dirty phase of development and transition to sustainable sources of energy. In other words, we need you."

U.S. President Barack Obama,
UC Irvine Commencement Address, June 14, 2014

Chapter 4

THE NET ZERO CATAPULT

Sometimes, gathering the data you need to produce a Carbon Reduction Plan can take a long time, and the Net Zero catapult is a useful tool for tackling this and getting up and running quickly. It is particularly useful to help you discover early in the process whether there might be problems with certain aspects of the data, and gives you a feel for the size and shape of your carbon footprint.

The software should have a catapult process like this built into it already, but if not, follow this recipe to run through your catapult:

1. Estimate your gas, electricity and oil use by looking at the average cost of each. Then, multiply this by the relevant carbon factor for each energy source
2. Estimate the number of flights you take for domestic, short-haul and long-haul, and multiply that by the typical carbon footprint of each of those flight types
3. Estimate the number of deliveries you receive each week and what type of deliveries they are, whether van, truck, car and so on. Then multiply that by the carbon factor for each delivery of that type
4. Do the same for the deliveries you make to your clients
5. Using the square footage of your site(s), estimate the amount of waste a business of that type and size would generate
6. Multiply the number of vans operated by an average amount of carbon emitted per van per year
7. Repeat this for cars, lorries and electric cars
8. Using the square footage and type of organisation (or number of pupils, number of patients, number of beds, and so on), estimate the carbon footprint of typical purchases such as paper, laptops and screens

Using this procedure, a software package can quickly estimate your carbon footprint, typically with an accuracy of approximately ±100%. Of course, this is not accurate and makes all sorts of assumptions - There is no such thing as *'average number of miles driven by lorries'*. However, the benefits of getting an early handle on your footprint outweigh the drawbacks. Once you have your estimated footprint, you can then concentrate on refining and improving it using the full MARTOC method shown in forthcoming chapters.

Note that you cannot use the catapult for the certification aspect for Net Zero. It's an excellent starting point, but requires refining using the MARTOC method before you consider certification.

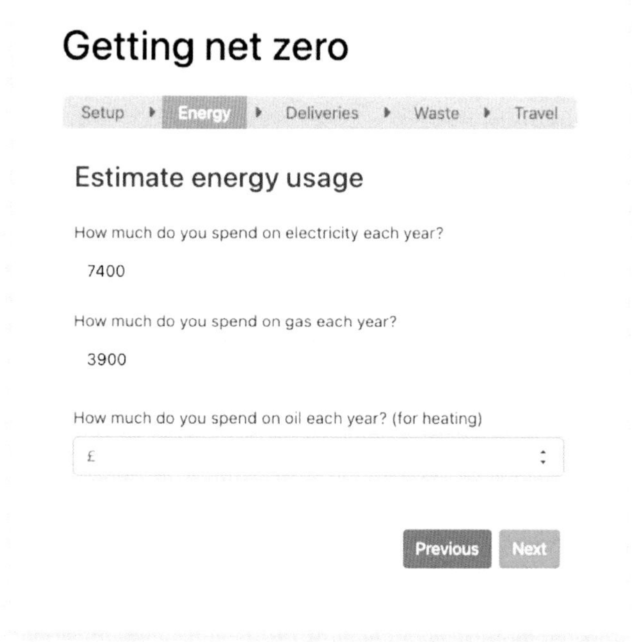

Getting net zero

Setup ▸ Energy ▸ Deliveries ▸ Waste ▸ Travel

Estimate energy usage

How much do you spend on electricity each year?

7400

How much do you spend on gas each year?

3900

How much do you spend on oil each year? (for heating)

£

Previous Next

Figure 11: A typical data entry page for an online Net Zero catapult system. This is part of a sequence of approximately 15 screens that ask similar types of questions to estimate your business' carbon footprint.

Chapter 5

STRUCTURING YOUR CARBON REDUCTION PLAN

A Carbon Reduction Plan normally consists of six main sections plus an introduction by someone senior to set the scene. This structure closely follows the MARTOC methodology described previously, and, by way of a reminder, the sections are:

1. Introduction
2. Measurement of what your carbon footprint is
3. Your aims and target reduction goals
4. The projects you intend to implement to reduce your carbon emissions
5. Statements concerning how you have performed to date against the targets you have set
6. What you are doing to offset the emissions that remain, even after you have completed your reduction efforts
7. A statement of commitment from your senior management and details of what certifications you have obtained

Normally, a Carbon Reduction Plan is about 8-12[7] pages long . Whilst it includes summaries of what your carbon footprint is and what your targets are, it is not necessary to include the detailed calculations. These can stay either in the software or a separate reference document if you're doing it manually, and that way the report can remain concise.

7 For comparison, TCFD summary reports can be 60-70 pages long, ESOS summaries are typically 10-12 pages, SECR statements are half a page and SBTi application forms are around 70 pages.

Consider including images in your Carbon Reduction Plan to bring it to life. You might want to picture your senior manager in the introduction section, for example, and the offset and removals section of your plan may contain compelling images of some of the projects you have chosen to support.

The recommended sections for your Carbon Reduction Plan are described in more detail in the chapters below.

"The truth is: the natural world is changing. And we are totally dependent on that world. It provides our food, water and air. It is the most precious thing we have and we need to defend it."

David Attenborough

AN EXAMPLE CARBON REDUCTION PLAN

Leading the Change: A Message from the CEO

"At OASIS Garden Centre, we firmly believe that social and environmental considerations are integral to our values and purpose. We are dedicated to making a positive difference not only in nurturing nature but also in enriching our communities. Over the past year, we have heightened our focus on various social and environmental projects, driven by our mission to create a sustainable future.

To further intensify our efforts, we are proud to introduce our Environmental Policy Group. This dedicated team will guide and champion our environmental initiatives, empowering us to pursue our environmental ambitions with even greater vigour.

Our commitment extends beyond the boundaries of our garden centre. We aim to create an environment that not only protects and enhances nature but also cares for the well-being of our community at large. From promoting eco-friendly gardening practices to engaging in community outreach programs, we are dedicated to making a positive impact.

Together, let's sow the seeds of positive change and cultivate a greener, more vibrant community."

Jamie Brown

Jamie Brown
CEO at OASIS Garden Centre

Contents

Measure

Baseline Emissions

Baseline emissions are a record of the greenhouse gases that have been produced n the past - before introducing any strategies to reduce emissions – and are the eference point against which emission eductions can be measured.

2018 was the first year where we had a omplete GHG inventory, required for PPN 6/21 compliance. OASIS has not previously aselined emissions, therefore, this eporting year will be the baseline. Reasonable assumptions are made in alculating the Scope 3 emissions for this eriod.

Annual emissions: April 2022 - March 2023	
Emissions	TOTAL (tCO2e)
Scope 1	52
Scope 2	29
Scope 3 (Including Sources)	782
Total Emissions	**866**

Carbon Calculation Assumptions

As part of our employee commuting measurements, we have included working from home data to give a better view of our total emissions.

To calculate the commuting and working from home emissions we sent a survey to our staff. We had a response rate of 41% and to cover the whole period we extrapolated this data.

Emissions Breakdown

s part of our ongoing commitment to sustainability, we have conducted a omprehensive analysis of our emissions. This breakdown provides a transparent view our Scope 1, 2, and 3 emissions, enabling us to understand and address our nvironmental impact more effectively.

Scope 1	Emissions TOTAL (tCO2e)
Company-Owned hicles	52
tal Emissions Scope 1	**52**

Scope 2	Emissions TOTAL (tCO2e)
Energy – Electricity	29
al Emissions Scope 2	**29**

Scope 3	Emissions TOTAL (tCO2e)
3.04: Deliveries (Upstream)	202
3.05: Waste generated in operations	0.2
3.06: Business Travel	103
3.07: Commuting and Home-working	22
3.09: Deliveries (Downstream)	477
Total Emissions Scope 3	**804**

Total Emissions	886 tCO2e
Intensity Ratio	3.8 tCO2e per person

Aims and Targets

Driving Emissions Reduction: A Sustainable Approach

OASIS is committed to a 100% reduction in all Scope 1, 2, and 3 emissions by 2030, through ambitious carbon reduction projects. Our target is to reduce our carbon emissions by 45% by 2030 compared to our 2018 figures. Our focus is on proactively minimising our carbon footprint rather than relying solely on offsetting emissions. We firmly believe that taking direct action to reduce emissions is the most effective approach.

To ensure accountability and progress, we will collaborate closely with our partners to establish an annua emission reduction target. This key performance indicator (KPI) will be seamlessly integrated into ou robust reporting system, enabling us to monitor and track our progress towards meeting our targets yea after year.

We recognise the importance of continuous improvement and will proactively seek innovative solutions t further reduce our environmental impact. By prioritising emission reduction projects and closely monitorin our performance, we are committed to fostering a more sustainable future for our garden centre and th wider community.

Together, we can make a significant difference in mitigating our environmental impact and creating greener world for generations to come.

Reduction Projects

Towards a Low-Carbon Future

We are proud to share our achievements in implementing various carbon reduction projects. These initiatives align with our commitment to reducing emissions and advancing sustainability within our operations. Through these efforts, we aim to make a positive impact on the environment and inspire others to join us on the path towards a greener future. Here are some notable carbon reduction projects we have successfully completed.

Carbon Reduction Projects

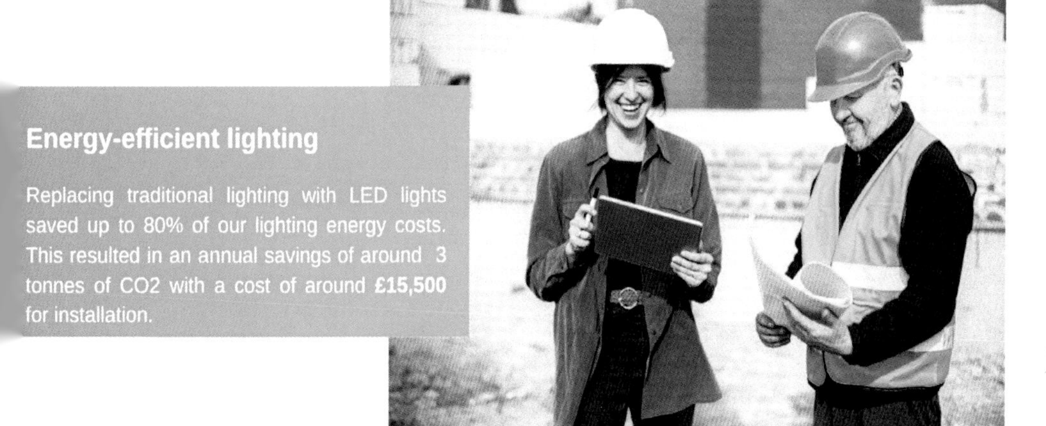

Energy-efficient lighting

Replacing traditional lighting with LED lights saved up to 80% of our lighting energy costs. This resulted in an annual savings of around 3 tonnes of CO_2 with a cost of around **£15,500** for installation.

Upgrade to energy-efficient appliances:

Our plans to upgrade to energy-efficient appliances such as refrigerators, air conditioners, and heaters will save up to 30% of energy costs. This will result in an annual savings of around 3.7 tonnes of CO_2 with a cost of around **£3,000** for installation per appliance.

Carbon Reduction Projects (Continued)

Waste Management & Composting

We are implementing a comprehensive waste management and composting system to enable us to minimize waste sent to landfills and reduce associated greenhouse gas emissions. We are establishing recycling programs for plastic, paper, and other materials, as well as composting initiatives for organic waste. By diverting waste from landfills and turning it into nutrient-rich compost, we contribute to a circular economy and mitigate greenhouse gas emissions.

Insulate the building:

Better insulation of the building will reduce heat loss and save up to 25% of energy costs. This should result in an annual savings of around 1.5 tonnes of CO2 with a cost of approximately £22,500 for the installation.

Install programmable thermostats

Programmable thermostats can help to control heating and cooling systems and save up to 10% of energy costs. This can result in an annual savings of around 1.4 tonnes of CO2 with a cost of around £500 for installation per device.

Use natural lighting

Maximizing the use of natural lighting can reduce the need for artificial lighting and save up to 20% of our lighting costs. This will result in an annual savings of around 3 tonnes of CO2 with no installation cost.

Conduct an energy audit

Conducting an energy audit can identify areas of energy waste and help to develop an energy-saving plan. This can result in an annual savings of around 5 tonnes of CO2 with a cost of around £2,000 for the audit.

Tracking Emissions

Our Continuous Improvement Plan

Data-Driven Decision Making

We understand the importance of tracking progress year on year to ensure our carbon reduction plan remains effective and aligned with our sustainability goals. Through continuous monitoring, we can evaluate the impact of our initiatives, identify areas for improvement, and make necessary adjustments to our plan. By closely monitoring our carbon emissions, energy usage, and other relevant metrics, we can measure our progress and make informed decisions to further optimise our sustainability efforts.

Actual vs Target Carbon Emissions

Reduce carbon by 45% by 2030 compared to 2018 figures

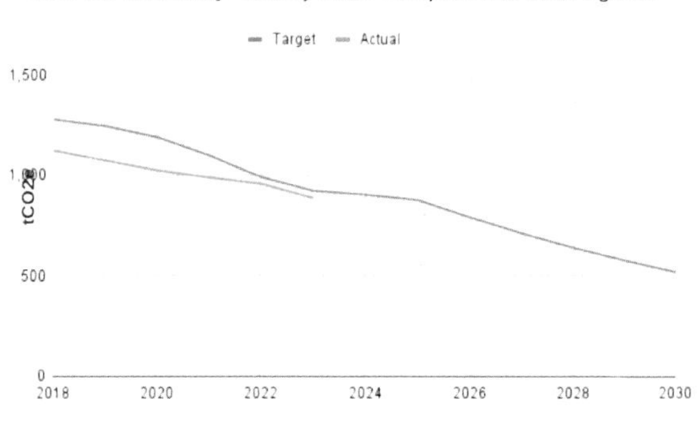

We have had difficulties measuring our Scope 3 emissions, in particular those associated with our supply chain. This year we are developing a Supplier Portal, and a Supplier Handbook to help our suppliers engage more with our sustainability journey.

Carbon Intensity

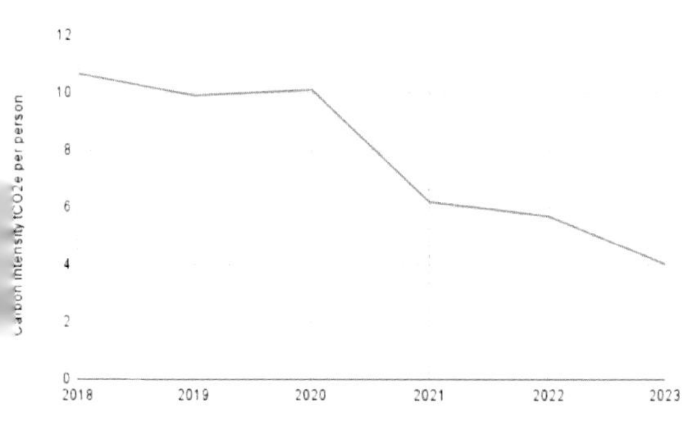

Year	2018	2019	2020	2021	2022	2023
Staff	120	126	118	178	174	230
Emissions (tCO_2e)	1,124	1,073	1,023	988	957	886

Measuring and Monitoring Carbon Intensity

Carbon intensity is a crucial metric that measures the greenhouse gas emissions produced per staff member and allows us to compensate for our new extension in 2021 and our acquisition of Border's Garden Centre in 2023. In each of these cases, our operations increased significantly. Due to the hard work of our sustainability team, however, not only did our overall carbon footprint decrease, but our carbon intensity continued to fall as well.

We will continue to focus on our carbon intensity as our primary metric in relation to our operations to help us identify areas of improvement and implement targeted strategies to decrease our carbon intensity.

Offsetting

OASIS

Offsetting Emissions: Investing in a Greener Future

As part of our carbon reduction strategy, we offset any remaining emissions through carbon offset projects verified according to "The Gold Standard". These initiatives support environmental conservation, renewable energy, reforestation, and other efforts that reduce greenhouse gas emissions. By participating in credible offsetting programs, we take responsibility for our carbon footprint and contribute to the global fight against climate change. Our dedication to offsetting ensures a Net Zero carbon footprint and a greener future for all.

The amount we need to offset this year is **886 tCO2e**

Reforestation Initiative

Through our partnership with a local environmental organisation, we support a reforestation project that aims to restore and expand woodland areas in our region. By planting trees, we not only offset our carbon emissions but also contribute to habitat restoration, biodiversity conservation, and the improvement of air quality in our community.
In 2023, we offset 433 tonnes, which was half of our total emissions, and donated a total of £12,000 to the initiative.

Conservation & Wildlife Protection

Through our partnership with a conservation organisation, we support projects aimed at protecting vulnerable ecosystems and wildlife habitats in rural Uganda. These projects involve habitat restoration, species conservation, and biodiversity preservation.
In 2023, we offset 433 tonnes of our emissions and donated a total of £6,500.

Community Green Spaces

We support the creation and maintenance of community green spaces in urban areas. These projects involve converting unused or neglected spaces into vibrant green areas, such as parks, gardens, and urban forests. By revitalizing these spaces, we enhance local biodiversity, improve air quality, and provide accessible and tranquil areas for the community to enjoy.
We donated £5,000 to this project

In total, we have donated **£23,500** to sustainability projects in **2023**

Commitment & Certification

Net Zero Declaration and Sign-Off

This Carbon Reduction Plan has been completed in accordance with PPN 06/21. Additional optional sections have been added to include our Supply Chain Emissions and our Offsetting and Removals initiatives.

Emissions have been reported in accordance with PPN 06/21 and the GHG Reporting Protocol standard. Scope 1, Scope 2, and Scope 3 emissions have been calculated using the official DEFRA-approved conversion factors for 2022/2023 in accordance with the PPN 06/21 and Net Zero methodologies.

Supply chain emissions (Scope 3) have been reported in accordance with both Net Zero standards and The GHG Corporate Value Chain (Scope 3) Corporate and Accounting Standard.

We have not applied for external Net Zero Certification this year, but are considering this for next year.

This Carbon Reduction Plan has been reviewed and approved by the Board of Directors for OASIS Garden Centre Limited.

Signed J Brightly

Position Jo Brightly, Operations Director

Date 27 May 2023

Chapter 6

INTRODUCTION AND EXECUTIVE SUMMARY

Carbon Reduction Plan Section One

At the beginning of the Carbon Reduction Plan, you should include a cover page and introduction.

In some plans, such as illustrated below, there is no real introduction and you just jump straight into the plan details. In others, this section can include a quote by senior management summarising the company's Net Zero strategy and detailing some key highlights of the work you have done so far to reduce your emissions, alongside the key focus areas for your sustainability journey over the coming years. It is a good idea to include an introduction, as sometimes this is the only section people will read, especially if they are not as invested in the Net Zero journey as you are.

CARBON REDUCTION PLAN FRONT PAGE EXAMPLE

Company name:	My Green Company Ltd
Publication date:	8 May 2023

Commitment to achieving Net Zero

GreenCo PLC is committed to achieving Net Zero emimssions by 2032.

Baseline Emissions Footprint

Baseline emissions are a record of the greenhouse gases that have been produced in the past and were produced prior to the introduction of any strategies to reduce emissions. Baseline emissions are the reference point against which emissions reduction can be measured.

Our baseline year is 2022.

Baseline Year 2022	
Additional Details relating to the Baseline Emissions calculations	
2021/2022 was the first year where wo had a complete GHG inventory, required for PPN 06/21 compliance, has not previously baselined emissions. Therefore, this current reporting year will be the baseline. Reasonable assumptions are made in calculating the Scope 3 emissions for this period.	
Baseline year emissions:	
EMISSIONS	TOTAL (tCO2e)
Scope 1	173
Scope 2	781
Scope 3 (Included Supply Chain)	303
Total Emissions	1257

Figure 12: *An example front page of a Carbon Reduction Plan.*

"Solving the climate crisis is the greatest and most complex challenge that homo sapiens have ever faced. The main solution, however, is so simple that even a small child can understand it. We have to stop our emissions of greenhouse gases."

Greta Thunberg

Chapter 7

MEASURING YOUR CARBON FOOTPRINT

Carbon Reduction Plan Section Two

You've got your software up and running, you've got a team set up, you know roughly what your carbon footprint is via the Net Zero catapult. Now, it's time to start work on the detailed data processing required to calculate your carbon footprint.

You're going to need monthly data for the following items for the past financial year:

- Electricity, gas, and oil – normally obtained either from paper bills, online portals or imported directly from the supplier electronically if your software supports it.
- Petrol and diesel used in company vehicles - normally either collected from your fuel cards if you use them, or estimated from company car mileage records.
- Supply chain details, i.e., what you buy – normally obtained from your accounting package or via a direct link to your accounting package if your software supports it.
- Business travel – train journeys, taxi journeys, flights, hotel stays, staff mileage and so on. These are normally collected from receipts, invoices and, in the case of staff mileage, your expenses system (for paper-based systems, you might consider processing receipts on a sampling basis, i.e. doing half of the expense claims and doubling the result).
- Deliveries coming to you – online orders, stock and so on – normally calculated by counting the number of receipts and invoices you get
- Deliveries you make – most companies have records of this in the sales system.

- Waste – estimated if it is not significant or detailed out for larger amounts, normally with data supplied by your waste processing company (most waste processors are getting better at this these days and the level of detail we can now get is significantly better than it used to be).
- Commuting and work from home – normally done via a staff survey.

In some cases, getting monthly data for each of these categories may be problematic. You may also use annual data, though monthly is better at showing up trends and problem areas that are not as obvious if you rely on annual data. This is especially true if you have some data components that contain months in which the data spikes unaccountably in some months or has some months in which it was zero. Annual data alone would not show up either of these issues.

Figure 13: A typical carbon footprint measurement given by one of the online Net Zero catapult systems. Note the splitting of the carbon footprint into its different constituent components.

GAS AND ELECTRICITY

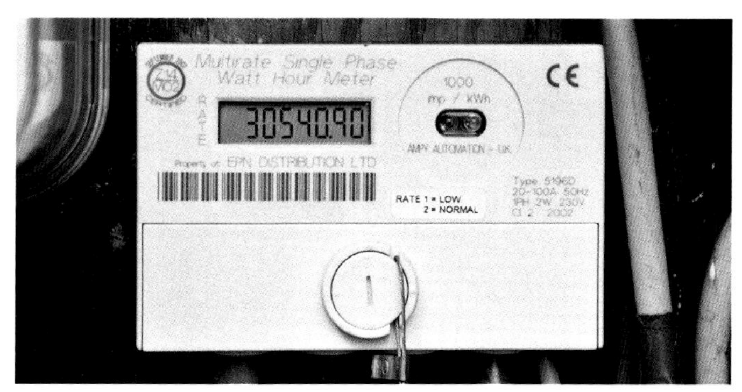

Figure 14: A typical UK electricity meter. Photo credit: Canva.

When you come to measuring your electricity and gas use, there are three ways of doing it:

1. In the past, you would have collected all your bills for your site, printed them off and manually entered them into the software. Now, there are more efficient ways of doing it.
2. Another option is to vist your utility provider's website and download a full breakdown of your use. It normally takes a degree of setting up, but it is then straightforward to download a file from their online portal which you can upload into your software in CSV format.
3. Alternatively, your software will ideally have links built into it to access the utility companies' energy databases directly, so you can import the data you need automatically.

Whichever method you use, when entering your data into the software it is important to do this according to kilowatt hours (kWh) usage. If you use monetary amounts, such as what you paid each month, this might be an inaccurate representation of your energy use as bill totals generally include service charges, capacity charges, administrative charges and so on.

An example carbon calculation for renewable electricity

Silvia signs a new deal for her flower shop with the utility company and moves across to "100% renewable energy sourced by wind". Whether it is onshore or offshore is not specified and we're going to assume it's onshore.

Her carbon emissions were:

tCO2e = [number of kWh used] x [carbon factor per kWh for renewable energy]

tCO2e = 65311 x 0.011 kgCO2e = 718 kgCO2e = 0.7 tCO2e

RENEWABLE ENERGY

Figure 15: Renewable energy might not be what you think it is. Always check exactly what you are buying when you sign up to green electricity schemes and look at who verifies or certifies what your electricity company is telling you. Source: BBC.

You might think that emissions from renewable energy sources are zero, and that you can put all your emissions at 0 kgCO2e. Sadly, that is not the case.

The problem is threefold:

1. You must move the energy from where it is produced to your offices. This involves power lines, which have electrical resistance, so you lose some energy along the way in the form of heat. It is small, but it's not zero.[8]
2. Some so-called 'renewable energy sources' stretch the definition of what might reasonably be considered renewable. One example is steam-generator power stations that burn pellets made of sawdust from trees cut down in Canada and shipped across the Atlantic[xvii]. When you imagine wind turbines turning serenely on

8 This is known in the trade as 'Transmission and Distribution Losses' and was 0.01769 kgCO2e per kWh in the UK in2022. Source: UK Government

the hills of the Lake District, what you might actually be getting is smoke-belching freighters lumbering across the Atlantic.

3. Renewable energy generating equipment, such as solar cells and wind turbines, must be produced, installed, and maintained. This does not emit much carbon in the scheme of things, but it is not zero.

There is a fourth problem here, although rather technical. When companies commit to providing '100% renewable energy', most generally only mean that, annually, they buy enough renewable energy to cover their renewable requirements for the year. They do not guarantee that the energy used on a site at a specific hour of a specific day was from renewable sources. The actual energy used at any given moment could easily have come from a gas or coal power station, despite purchasing 'certified green energy'.

Without the emissions caused by moving the energy around, the true emissions from various renewable energy sources are shown below[xviii].

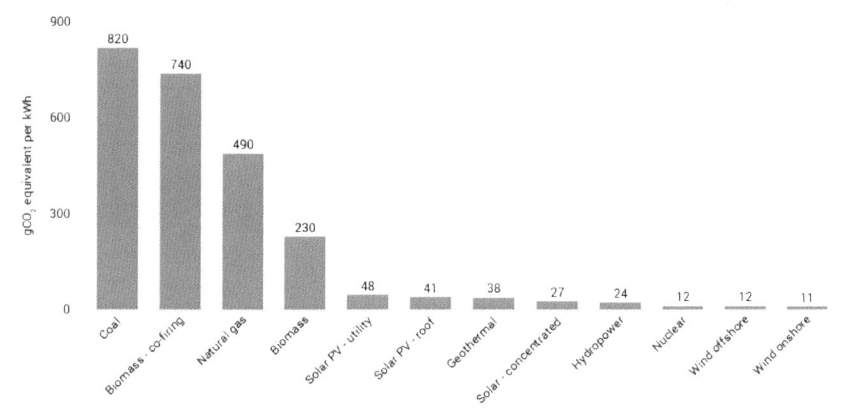

Figure 16: Emissions from different renewable energy sources. Source: World Nuclear Association.

An example carbon calculation for renewable electricity

Silvia signs a new deal for her flower shop with the utility company and moves across to "100% renewable energy sourced by wind". Whether it is onshore or offshore is not specified and we're going to assume it's onshore.

Her carbon emissions were:

tCO2e = [number of kWh used] x [carbon factor per kWh for renewable energy]

$tCO2e = 65311 \times 0.011\ kgCO2e = 718\ kgCO2e = 0.7\ tCO2e$

THE PROBLEMS OF READING A GAS BILL

If you cannot download a spreadsheet from your supplier for your gas bills, and you must enter data from the bills themselves, this can be problematic.

What we know of as 'gas' is actually a mix of gasses[9], and utility companies frequently change the proportion of these gasses that they supply to you. Gas meters only measure the gas supplied in volumetric units such as cubic metres or cubic feet, and do not measure the mix of high-energy gasses and low-energy gasses.

On your energy bill, there is therefore a 'calorific correction factor', which is the average energy content of the gas that was supplied for that month. To calculate the kWh of energy used, you must account not only for the volume of gas you consumed, but also this correction factor. This sounds complicated, but you will typically find that this calculation is done for you and the kWh figures are supplied on the bill.

9 This is caused by the gas suppliers varying the proportion of methane, butane and hydrogen in the gas they deliver, probably because their gas comes from different sources at different times.

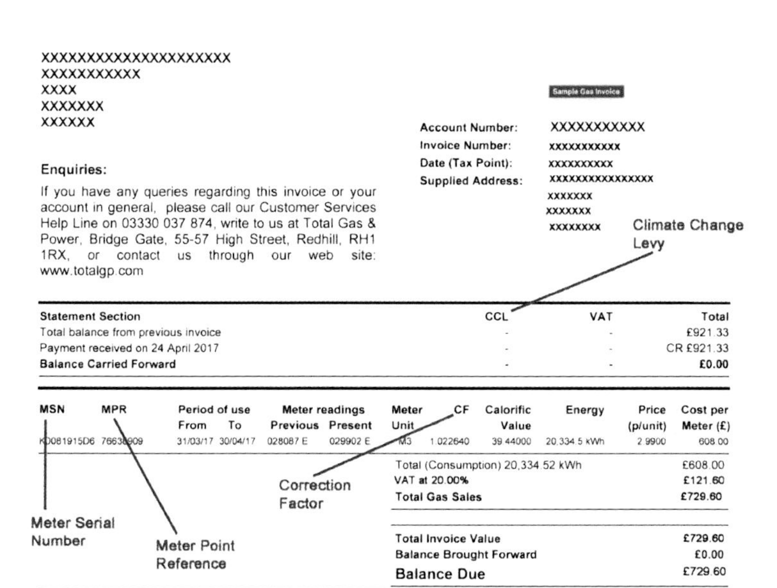

TOTAL GAS & POWER

Gas Invoice
Page 1 of 2

XXXXXXXXXXXXXXXXXXXXX
XXXXXXXXXXX
XXXX
XXXXXXX
XXXXXX

Sample Gas Invoice

Account Number:	XXXXXXXXXXX
Invoice Number:	XXXXXXXXXXX
Date (Tax Point):	XXXXXXXXXX
Supplied Address:	XXXXXXXXXXXXXXXX
	XXXXXXX
	XXXXXXX
	XXXXXXXX

Enquiries:

If you have any queries regarding this invoice or your account in general, please call our Customer Services Help Line on 03330 037 874, write to us at Total Gas & Power, Bridge Gate, 55-57 High Street, Redhill, RH1 1RX, or contact us through our web site: www.totalgp.com

Statement Section	CCL	VAT	Total
Total balance from previous invoice	-	-	£921.33
Payment received on 24 April 2017	-	-	CR £921.33
Balance Carried Forward	-	-	**£0.00**

MSN	MPR	Period of use From	To	Meter readings Previous	Present	Meter Unit	CF	Calorific Value	Energy	Price (p/unit)	Cost per Meter (£)
K0081915D6	7663[illegible]909	31/03/17	30/04/17	028087 E	029902 E	M3	1.022640	39.44000	20,334.5 kWh	2.9900	608.00

Total (Consumption) 20,334.52 kWh	£608.00
VAT at 20.00%	£121.60
Total Gas Sales	**£729.60**
Total Invoice Value	**£729.60**
Balance Brought Forward	£0.00
Balance Due	£729.60

Continued on next page...

Figure 17: An example gas bill showing the calorific correction factor (CF) which converts gas volume supplied into kWh. Photo credit: Total Gas & Power.

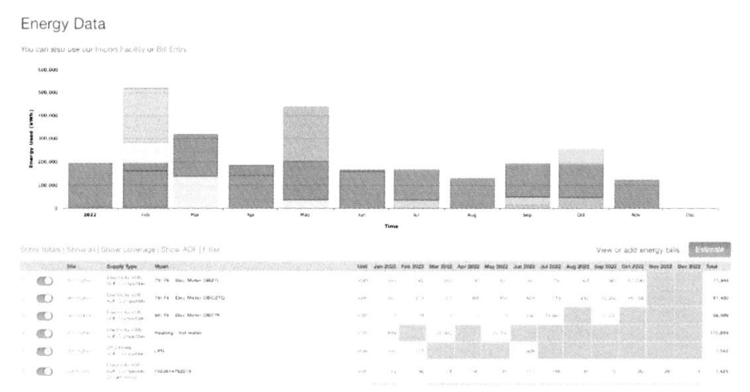

Figure 18: A typical data entry screen for entering electricity and gas data into an online platform. This screen is taken from Enistic Enterprise Edition.

HOW ACCURATE IS THE DATA? ESTIMATES USED BY UTILITY COMPANIES

You would be forgiven for thinking that your utility bills are 100% accurate. If you have a smart meter, your usage is much more likely to be accurate, but if not, it's likely that your energy company has used estimates to calculate your bill.

Let's imagine you do not have a smart meter and instead provide your own readings to your utility company to calculate your bill. If you did that twice per year, you can see that the energy used in between those times as shown on your monthly bills is always going to be an estimate, rather than a reflection of your actual usage.

The way energy companies deal with this is by looking at historic data from the users in your area and estimating your bills based on what you used previously, as well as what other companies in your area typically use. They are normally reasonably accurate (and the more frequently you can provide readings to them, the more accurate they will be), but remember that, unless you have a smart meter, you are always going to be using estimates for your energy use.

OVERCOMING ISSUES WITH MISSING DATA

Most of the companies that I look after have gaps in their data of some form. It is fair to say that the better organised a company is, the fewer gaps they will encounter, but realistically you are likely to have data gaps. In these circumstances, you must estimate what the missing data would have been.

If you have a couple of months of missing data, either use common sense or an average to fill in those gaps. Make a note that you have used estimations and will have access to more accurate data in subsequent years. This way, you can plug your data gaps quickly and avoid holding up your Net Zero process. If you have a significant amount of data missing, you could estimate the missing data if you feel confident that the estimates are going to be meaningful. Alternatively, you might consider flagging this as an urgent issue that needs resolving before you travel any further on your Net Zero journey.

In terms of how much data it is appropriate to estimate, it really depends on the standard you are following. Some standards, such as the UK Government's SECR standard, are extremely strict and only allow you to estimate up to 3% of the data (though less than 2% is desirable). Others, such as PPN/0621, are less strict. Whilst there isn't any defined maximum amount of data you can estimate, you should try to keep it under 10% if you can.

When we mention percentages in reference to these gaps, we don't mean counting the number of data gaps - we mean considering the quantity of estimated energy used in the calculation of the overall total energy consumption. If you had two electricity meters, for example, one of which only supplies a very small amount of energy and the other a great deal, it is more appropriate to have gaps in the small electricity meter's data than in the larger supply meter.

The exceptions to these accuracy rules are the Scope 3 data items. By their very nature, these are more problematic to process, so you should aim to be at least 70% accurate with this data. In reality, I regularly see Scope 3 data with far worse accuracy than this - but that is often the best we can do until Scope 3 is more accurately understood by the companies in your supply chain. In these cases, simply make a note of the problem, be transparent about the issue in your Carbon Reduction Plan and look to improve the situation in subsequent reports.

FOR GREATER ACCURACY, FIT A SMART METER

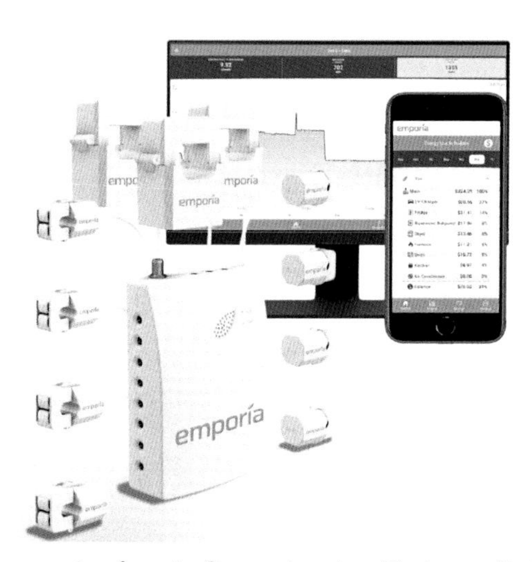

Figure 19: An example of a retrofit smart meter. Photo credit: Amazon.

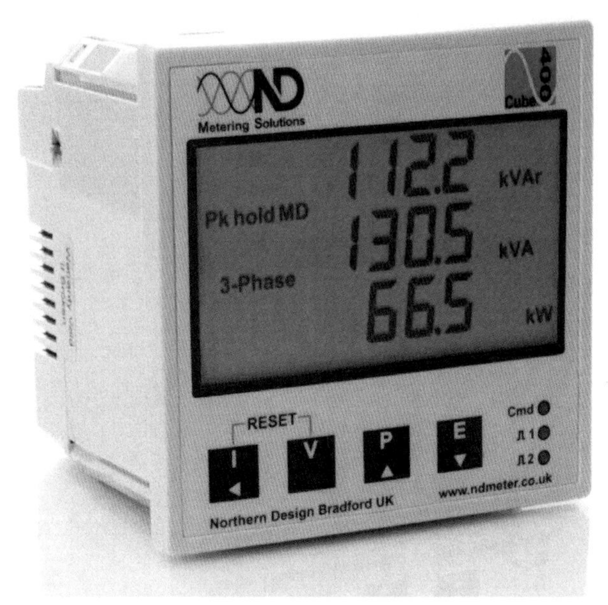

Figure 20: A commercial grade smart meter, which we have fitted in the Enistic offices and which provides exact information about the amount of energy used. Photo credit: ND Metering.

If you haven't already got a smart meter, I highly recommend you get one to better track your energy use. There is an installation cost, but they are typically not expensive and retrofit systems are available if a new primary meter is not an option. A smart meter will stop the problems associated with estimation and enable you to know precisely what you use.

If you begin work to reduce your electricity use, only having monthly estimated data is going to cause you all sorts of problems. Knowing precisely how much you saved by fitting a smart meter will allow you to have quick and accurate feedback about what's happening and whether your project is working or not. A smart meter is also essential if you want to carry out a baseload analysis, which is an effective energy saving exercise (covered in more detail later in the book).

COMPANY VEHICLES

If you have good records for your company vehicles, this section is relatively straightforward to complete, although incomplete records can make it problematic. As such, if you don't have good record keeping systems in place now, it's time to think about improving them.

The basic calculation we will use is:

tCO2e (vehicles) = [litres of diesel & petrol used] x [carbon factor per litre]

As you can see, if you have good records showing the amount of fuel you have purchased – for example, records from company fuel cards – then this is straightforward.

Example diesel carbon calculation

Brett works for a paper manufacturer which ships its paper on rolls to a processing plant using flat-bed trucks, which last year consumed 18,480 litres of diesel.

His carbon emissions from these journeys were:

tCO2e = 18480 x [carbon emissions per litre of diesel]

= 18480 x 2.56 kgCO2e = 47,309 kgCO2e = 47 tCO2e

Sometimes, you won't have kept a record of the fuel used, but it is likely that you have a record of the mileage travelled. In this case, which is common, you will have to resort to looking at the official tables which convert truck mileage to CO2. These factors are less accurate than diesel conversion figures, as they make various assumptions about the miles per gallon of the truck, the way it was driven, traffic conditions, the degree of loading of the truck and so on. If possible, it is therefore better to use the amount of fuel used rather than mileage conversion factors.

Example mileage carbon calculation

Peter's finance team says that their new IT system does not have the records of the amount of fuel purchased. However, they do have the mileage records from the operations manager, who uses a spreadsheet to record monthly truck mileages. He finds that the total number of miles travelled for all the trucks was 207,131.

His carbon emissions from these trucks were:

tCO2e = 207131 x [carbon emissions per mile for a 5 tonne flat-bed truck]

= 207131 x 0.74574 kgCO2e = 154,000 kgCO2e = 154 tCO2e

Some companies do not record mileage or fuel consumption at all. In these cases: (a) remedy the situation as soon as possible and begin to record these figures; and (b) use the fuel expenditure in £ to calculate the amount of fuel used. As you might imagine, this requires knowing, or at least estimating, what the average cost per litre of fuel was for the year, which can be problematic, especially as fuel prices fluctuate rapidly.

Example carbon calculation based on expenditure

Suzie runs a car parts business. She doesn't keep many records, but she does know that last year she spent £72,518 on petrol for her fleet of three vans.

Her carbon emissions from these vans were:

tCO_2e = (72518 / [average price per litre]) x [carbon emissions per litre of petrol]

= (72518 / 1.42) x 2.16 $kgCO_2e$ = 51,069 * 2.16 $kgCO_2e$ = 110,000 $kgCO_2e$ = 110 tCO_2e

If you have different types of vehicle, you should either:

1. use an average figure for all vehicles, which is quicker but less accurate; or
2. process each vehicle separately, which your software should be able to do for you automatically.

ELECTRIC AND HYBRID VEHICLES

Finally, a note about electric and hybrid vehicles. They should be processed in the normal way using the standard conversion factors that the government provides, which can convert miles travelled to CO_2. Alternatively, you can just use software to do it for you.

Example electric car carbon calculation

Toby runs a consultancy company and offers an incentive scheme for his senior team to subsidise the purchase of an electric company car if they want one. 12 employees have taken advantage of the offer. He has installed three charging points at his office which are well utilised, although nine of those 12 people work remotely and charge their cars at home. The total number of business miles travelled by the nine working remotely was 163,089 miles in the previous year.

His carbon emissions from these cars were:

tCO_2e = [carbon emissions from the cars charged at work] + [carbon emissions for the cars charged remotely]

= 0 (the electricity used for this was already processed in the Scope 2 calculations) + [miles travelled for the remote vehicles] x [emissions per mile]

= 0 + 163089 x 0.07192 kgCO2e = 11,729 kgCO2e = 11.7 tCO2e

A NOTE ON THE CARBON USED TO MANUFACTURE CARS AND TRUCKS

You might reasonably ask:

> *"What about all the emissions produced when the cars and trucks are manufactured and delivered to us in the first place?"*

It is certainly a valid point to make. In Net Zero, this is accounted for in the supply chain section if the cars are purchased but ignored if they are leased (with the leasing company accruing these emissions rather than the lessee). Currently, in Net Zero any emissions caused by the scrapping the vehicle at the end of its useful life are ignored[10].

AN INTRODUCTION TO SCOPE 3

So far, we have processed our gas, fuel and electricity under Scopes 1 and 2. Now, let's have a look at the most difficult scope to quantify: Scope 3. This relates to the carbon you cause other people to emit on your behalf ('indirect emissions').

Why should we bother looking at this? Well, quite simply, because Scope 3 emissions can be huge. One of my clients has 90% of their emissions in Scope 3, leaving only 10% in Scopes 1 and 2. With figures as large as this, it really can't be ignored.

10 An interesting calculation to do if you are bored one day, is to work out how many miles it takes the proud owner of a new electric car to travel before they offset the manufacturing and disposal emissions of the car. Spoiler alert: 27,000 miles is approximately right for one vehicle we analysed.

DEFINING THE BOUNDARY OF YOUR SCOPE 3 EMISSIONS

One of the main problems with Scope 3 calculations is deciding where to draw the line – figuring out what to include and in what level of detail. The example below illustrates this point.

An example of the complexity of Scope 3 emissions

Andy has asked his 10 best salespeople to fly to Berlin for a sales conference. The obvious elements of his carbon footprint for this would be:

- The carbon emitted by their diesel cars getting to the airport – Scope 1

- The carbon emitted from the plane during the flight – Scope 3

- The carbon emitted by the taxi at the other end of the journey – Scope 3

But what about ...

- The carbon emitted in producing the meal they had on the flight – Scope 3

- The emissions generated from cleaning the hotel room they stayed in and providing them with a lovely breakfast – Scope 3

- The emissions generated from building and maintaining the car park they used – Scope 3

- The emissions generated from producing the vodka that Mary knocked back a bit too much of when they went out during the first night – Scope 3

And even ...

- The carbon emitted during the manufacture of the cars they drove to the airport, the taxi, and the plane itself

- The carbon emitted when they designed the airport and then cleared the grassland that was there before they paved over it with concrete

Perhaps you can start to appreciate the problem here.

This problem is true for most companies, but is doubly problematic if you resell or manufacture items. If, for example, you buy and sell steel and turn it into table stands:

- Someone must locate some iron deposits and build a mine
- Someone must dig it up
- Someone must smelt it
- Someone must roll it
- Someone must then ship it to the warehouse
- Someone then must ship it to the retailer

All of those processes emit carbon and, in theory, all those emissions need to be included in our carbon footprint. Calculating these figures for one of your raw materials is complex, and doing it for all raw materials or products you buy is probably impractical.

Standards for processing Scope 3 data are developing rapidly, but it's fair to say that this important area of Net Zero still has a long way to go. I will provide guidelines for managing this complexity, where appropriate, as we go through the remainder of this chapter.

BREAKING DOWN THE SCOPE 3 SUB-SECTIONS

The six Scope 3 sub-sections we're going to include in our Carbon Reduction Plan are:

- 3.1 - supply chain
- 3.4 - deliveries you make to your clients
- 3.5 - the waste you generate
- 3.6 - business travel
- 3.7 - commuting and work from home
- 3.9 - deliveries you make to clients

Except for the supply chain section, these six sub-sections are what is required for compliance with PPN 06/21. In most cases, the remaining nine sub-sections are both difficult to calculate and largely insignificant anyway.

SUPPLY CHAIN

Supply chain emissions are the hardest part of most carbon footprint calculations. If you can get these sorted, the other sections of Scope 3 are going to be a breeze.

Supply chain emissions are defined as the carbon you cause to be emitted by your suppliers as a result of buying things from them. In theory, it is the sum of all emissions of your suppliers, all the carbon emissions of *their* suppliers, all the emissions of their suppliers and so forth, which is a truly difficult calculation to make.

Luckily, there are practical ways of making it manageable. To help simplify the problem, there are three things that can be done:

1. Group your suppliers according to how important they are to you; for example tier 1, tier 2, and tier 3
2. Tackle each group in a different way and at different stages of your Net Zero journey, dealing with the more important suppliers in the first year, the less important in the second year, and so on
3. Simplify calculation of the carbon emissions of the products you buy (see below)

When we start to tackle supply chain, software platforms start to become vital for helping to manage the large amount of data collection required from such a large and diverse group. If you haven't already taken the plunge and invested in a software platform, you may wish to start that process now.

SIMPLIFYING SUPPLY CHAIN EMISSIONS

There are three ways to calculate your supply chain emissions, and you can mix and match them as you see fit if it suits your circumstances:

1. Supplier-based factors – this is the default method to use unless one of the other methods stands out as more appropriate
2. Lifecycle analysis-based factors – use these only if you know the carbon footprint of the products you buy
3. Material-based factors – use these only if you buy raw materials

These were described in greater depth in Chapter 2, but to recap, supplier-based factors are usually my go-to method. This is largely due to a lack of accurate information about the carbon content of the vast majority of products on the market today. However, if I happen to have product data available or am dealing with a manufacturer, I use a combination of supplier-based and material-based analyses.

Example supply chain carbon calculation

Lottie runs a very simple office supply store that opens for 220 days per year, selling envelopes, pencils, coffee and milk.

- She spends £41,289 per year on rulers, envelopes and pencils, which she buys from a wholesaler with a carbon footprint of 31 tCO2e per annum and a turnover of £2.3 million.

- She spends £31,284 on coffee from a local roaster who has a carbon footprint of 71 tCO2e and a turnover of £345,000.

- She buys 18 litres of milk per day from the local farmer.

Lottie's carbon emissions for her supply chain are:

tCO2e (total) = tCO2e (envelopes and pencils) + tCO2e (milk) + tCO2e (coffee)

- tCO2e (envelopes and pencils) = [total amount she spent at wholesaler] * [carbon emissions of the wholesaler] / [turnover of the wholesaler] = 41289 * 31 / 2300000 = 0.55 tCO2e

- tCO2e (milk) = [litres of milk purchased] * [carbon emissions per litre of milk] = 18 * 220 * 1.39 = 5504 kgCO2e = 5.5 tCO2e

- tCO2e (coffee) = [value of coffee purchased] * [carbon emissions of the roaster] / [turnover of the roaster] = 31284 * 71 / 345000 = 6.4 tCO2e

So, the total emissions for Lottie's supply chain are:

0.55 + 5.5 + 6.4 = 12.45 tCO2e

To input your purchasing data into the system, these are most straightforward methods:

1. **CSV export from the accounting system** – export a list of everything you've bought in the past year by supplier, whether through your finance department (larger companies) or via a report called a 'purchase ledger' in your accounting system (smaller companies). This can then be uploaded into your software package.
2. **Automatically** – some platforms have automated links to some accounting platforms, so this import and processing can be done in the background automatically, which takes the pain out of the

process. If your software has this feature, I'd strongly recommend you use it

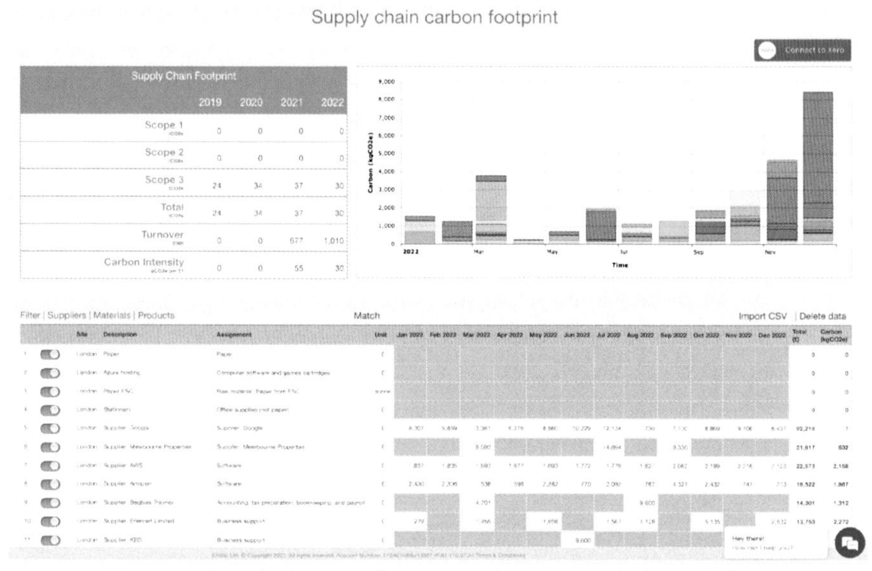

Figure 21: A typical screen for processing supply chain emissions. This screen is taken from Yeti. Note the 'Connect to Xero' button, which links directly to Xero accounting software.

WORKING WITH SUPPLIERS

Getting accurate supplier data for your Scope 3 emissions is not simple, and there are problems you are likely to face along the way. The major issues I've come across are detailed below, along with some tips on how to resolve them.

INCENTIVISING SUPPLIERS TO PARTICIPATE

Some suppliers simply don't care. You will ask them for a breakdown of the Scope 1, Scope 2 and Scope 3 emissions and they'll look at you like you're from outer space.

Try and encourage your suppliers to care, and if that fails, choose different suppliers. The long-term pressures from losing sales may be enough to encourage them to do the right thing in the end. If not, you can encourage participation from your suppliers in other ways.

It wouldn't be unusual for you to write a handbook for your suppliers. The handbook should explain the journey you are on and its importance to you. In it, you can explain how over time their requirement to participate will increase, moving from gentle encouragement to contract penalties, to eventual banishment.

This escalation of requirement to participate is becoming widespread here in the UK. By way of example, NHS suppliers:

- are now required to have a PPN 06/21-compliant Carbon Reduction Plan in place if the contract value is more than £5 million, and are encouraged to get one if they are under that threshold; and
- by 2027, *all* suppliers *must* have a compliant Carbon Reduction Plan in place if they wish to continue to supply to the NHS.

By taking this approach, over the next few years 80,000 NHS suppliers will be required to either get a Carbon Reduction Plan in place or risk losing their NHS sales.

MAKING IT EASY FOR SUPPLIERS TO NOTIFY YOU OF THEIR CARBON EMISSIONS

Some clients put in place supplier portals as well as supplier handbooks. These allow suppliers to submit their carbon emission and turnover details so you can easily calculate your share of their footprint, aka the supplier-based carbon factor.

The big daddy of these reporting portals is the Carbon Disclosure Project (CDP), which is an excellent initiative that centralises carbon emission disclosures across a wide range of industries, but often your carbon software will have one built in as well. If your software doesn't have a supplier portal built into it, it may have automatic links into the CDP instead.

WORKING WITH SUPPLIERS WHO HAVE ONLY JUST STARTED THEIR JOURNEY

Other suppliers may care about emissions, but may have only just started their Net Zero journey and not yet have accurate information to give you. This is the case with most suppliers we deal with: they're starting to get to grips with Scope 1 and Scope 2, but have not begun looking at Scope 3 in any detail. When they do, their overall carbon footprint is likely to increase significantly which, in turn, will throw out the calculations we are doing for our clients that rely on that data.

You may be able to use estimates for these suppliers, but this would be unusual. It could just be a case of just waiting and encouraging them to give you accurate figures when they are available. If you encounter this problem, make sure your senior management is aware things are likely to change significantly as these suppliers start to incorporate Scope 3 components.

WORKING WITH SUPPLIERS WHO WORK TO DIFFERENT STANDARDS

Some suppliers will measure their carbon footprint to a different standard to you. For example, you may have one supplier that always includes Scope 3 in their carbon footprint, and another that doesn't. This can be problematic if you want to choose suppliers with low carbon footprints to help you drive out emissions from your supply chain. As a result of different footprint standards, one supplier may look better than another on the face of things, but not because one is inherently more sustainable than the other. The way around this is to ask for all suppliers to follow a known standard, such as certified Net Zero.

CATEGORISING YOUR SUPPLIERS

It is useful to group your suppliers into different buckets to make the supply chain problem more manageable. Broadly speaking, you want to do more work with the suppliers that affect your carbon footprint more significantly than those that have a lower impact on it. We call each of these groups 'tiers', with tier 1 being very important to your business and tier 3 being of almost negligible importance.

Many companies will use common sense to group their suppliers into tiers. If you have got a long-established business, you probably know who your tier 1 suppliers are, and you can draw a ring around them easily enough from experience. You might also be able to draw a ring around the insignificant suppliers, from whom you buy relatively inexpensive things infrequently. You define them as your tier 3 suppliers, with all the suppliers that are left falling into the middle tier, or tier 2.

If it is not obvious who your tier 1, 2 and 3 suppliers are, consider grouping them by annual spend, with tier 1 including all those in the top 30% of your spend, tier 2 all those in the next 30% and tier 3 all those remaining.

Once grouped, you can deal with each of the groups in different ways. For example:

In year one:

- Tier 1 will be sent handbooks, encouraged to consider reporting their emissions in your supplier carbon portal and invited to educational briefings and online seminars
- Tier 2 will be sent handbooks and encouraged to consider reporting their emissions in your online supplier portal
- Tier 3 will be largely ignored

In year two:

- Tier 1 will be marked down in contract tenders if they have not submitted carbon emission data to you
- Tier 2 will be sent handbooks, encouraged to consider reporting their emissions in your online supplier portal and invited to educational briefings and online seminars
- Tier 3 will be largely ignored

In year three:

- Tier 1 will be barred from new contract tenders if they have not submitted certified Carbon Reduction Plans
- Tier 2 will be marked down in contract tenders if they have not submitted carbon emission data
- Tier 3 will be largely ignored

In year four:

- Tier 1 will be barred from new contract tenders if they have not submitted compliant Carbon Reduction Plans, and marked down in contracts if they have not shown significant reduction in their carbon emissions in line with their plan
- Tier 2 will be barred from new contract tenders if they have not submitted certified Carbon Reduction Plans
- Tier 3 will be largely ignored

This time-based approach of increasing levels of commitment towards sustainability from different groups of suppliers can be significant in reducing emissions and is a central pillar of global carbon reduction strategies. Large supply chains, such as car manufacturers and retail giants are, thankfully, embracing this. The changes they are requiring of their suppliers are proving to be a significant driver of change, and we get a significant number of enquiries that start with:

"We've been asked by a customer for a copy of our Carbon Reduction Plan but we don't have one, can you help?"

DELIVERIES YOU MAKE

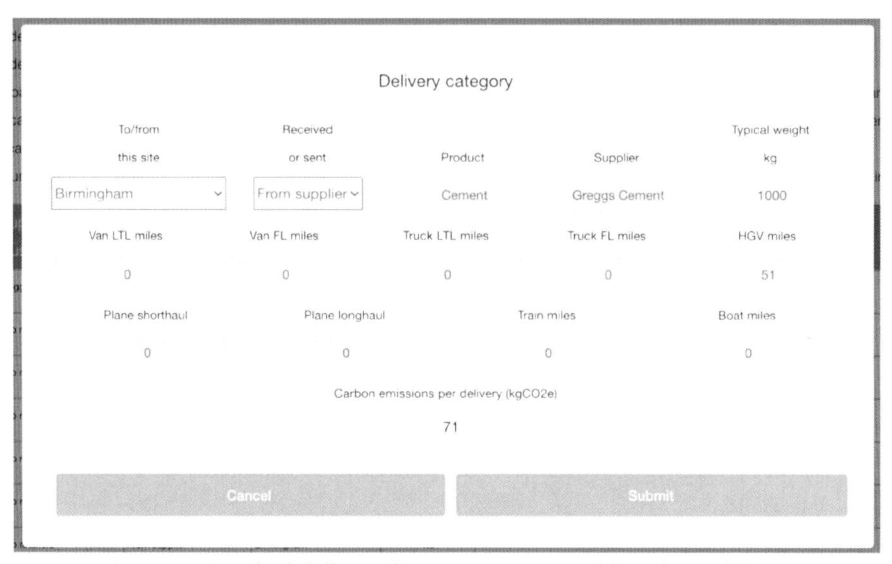

Figure 22: A typical delivery data entry screen asking about delivery methods. This screen is taken from the Enistic Enterprise Edition software platform, so shows more categories than are necessary for Net Zero.

If you don't deliver physical goods, you may choose to skip this section. You might send the occasional letter that does, technically, constitute a 'delivery', but unless you send a significant number of them, the footprint of the odd envelope or two can be ignored. This section is important for companies with ongoing, regular delivery operations.

If we consider the entire end-to-end process of delivering your items internationally, there will be many components of the journey that will be entirely outside of your control and, indeed, may change without your knowledge. For example, did your delivery to Taiwan go on its own plane, sitting alone and forlorn in the cargo bay, or was it crammed into a modern, fuel-efficient plane and then delivered for the last mile by a state-of-the art electric van? To make it practical to calculate the carbon footprint, we therefore ignore all international aspects of your deliveries, except if they are regular, well defined and significant (for example, if you are sending goods overseas by container or you are a retailer with a significant proportion of overseas customers).

To make the calculation possible, we also make assumptions when it comes to goods you deliver via courier companies such as UPS, DHL and DPD. In these instances, we use average carbon factors per package that the courier companies supply. For everything else, it is simply a case of recording the number of deliveries you make, the method of delivery and, if significant, their weight and size. It is acceptable to make extensive use of averages over time, and averages over package size if this makes it easier. Your software will give you the full range of options available, but typical carbon factors for deliveries are either:

- the distance your deliveries travel by van, truck, heavy goods vehicle and so on; or
- if your goods are particularly heavy, include the weight as well as the distance[11].

Typical carbon factors are shown in the table below.

Everyday items ordered over the internet · stationery, kitchen supplies, miscellaneous items

	kgCO2e
Average courier delivery*	0.181

	kgCO2e		
	Unit	Diesel	Petrol
Diesel van < 3.5 tonnes	tonne.km	0.57871	0.75394
	km	0.23156	0.21332
	miles	0.37268	0.3433

			kgCO2e		
	Unit	Empty	50% Laden	100% Laden	Average
Rigids	tonne.km		0.22924	0.13346	0.21345
	km	0.69215	0.82368	0.95522	0.84061
	miles	1.11389	1.32557	1.53726	1.35282

11 The 'distance travelled' calculation method assumes A->B vehicle journeys. It does not apply to modern 'hub and spoke' logistics methods, in which packages are picked up by van A, shipped to a central distribution hub and then delivered the last mile by another van. In these circumstances, use carbon factors supplied by the courier company to calculate your emissions.

	Unit	Empty	kgCO2e 50% Laden	100% Laden	Average
Artics	tonne.km		0.09674	0.06017	0.08153
	km	0.6563	0.8675	1.0787	0.92391
	miles	1.0562	1.3961	1.736	1.48688
HGVs	tonne.km		0.12145	0.07384	0.10614
	km	0.67032	0.84988	1.02944	0.89061
	miles	1.07877	1.36774	1.65671	1.43329

Figure 23: Carbon factors for deliveries you make or receive. Source: UK government

Example carbon calculation for the deliveries you make

Anna runs a printing company. Every day, she sends the printing she has done that day to her clients via a local courier, who uses a van to deliver her parcels.

The boxes vary in size, and the number of boxes per delivery varies depending on how large the job was. As each job has an invoice, it is straightforward for Anna to track how many orders were sent out, and she knows that last month she shipped 531 orders.

To enable her to calculate her footprint, she estimates that the average order contains two boxes which each weight approximately 7kg, and as she only delivers locally, each delivery is 3.7 miles on average.

As we are using shared transport (a van), we decide to use the distance travelled method of carbon calculation. The carbon footprint of Anna's deliveries is therefore:

[total distance travelled] x [carbon factor for van deliveries]

= [531] x [3.7] x [0.37268] kgCO2e = 732 kgCO2e

Note that in this example, the weight per box and number of boxes are immaterial. This is not always the case, and if you ship significantly bulky or heavy items you should take these into consideration using the tonne/km factors instead of the distance travelled method.

DELIVERIES YOU RECEIVE

The good news is that the method for calculating the carbon footprint of the things you get delivered to you is the same as for the deliveries you make to clients.

The only real difference is that companies tend not to keep adequate records of the number of deliveries they receive each month, and sometimes this makes the calculations less reliable. As a result, estimates are far more common when working out this component. In typical office situations, the carbon emissions of the occasional Amazon package are not material, and in many cases this estimation is not a problem.

If your incoming deliveries are significant and you do not record details of them, you should consider putting systems in place to start tracking them sooner rather than later.

Example carbon calculation for deliveries received

India runs a 50 person office in central Birmingham, and apart from the occasional new chair or desk, buys everything she needs on a day-to-day basis from the web. She doesn't have exact records, but estimates that they receive two or three deliveries per working day.

The carbon footprint for her incoming deliveries is:

[number of incoming deliveries from the web per year] x [carbon factor per web delivery]

= [2.5 x 5 x 52] x 0.181 kgCO2e = 650 x 0.181 = 118 kgCO2e = 0.1 tCO2e

WASTE

Calculating your carbon footprint for the waste you produce is relatively straightforward if you have the right data to hand – and if you use a professional waste company, they can normally provide this. If you don't have this data or your waste provider can't supply it, you may have a problem. This is especially true if you produce a mix of different waste types or a significant amount of waste, in which case you should consider putting waste measurement systems in place as a matter of urgency.

For most offices, waste is generally going to be a mix of paper and 'general waste'. Exceptions to this might be if you have some end-of-life kit that you're disposing of, or perhaps some old desks, carpet tiles or furniture from a re-modelling exercise. Whether you include these exceptional items or not is largely dependent on whether they are significant to your footprint or not. If they are, they should be included.

If you manufacture anything, the situation is more complex, and if your waste is significant, which in many cases it is, you should certainly think carefully when you come to process it.

To calculate your carbon footprint, your software will typically ask you to categorise your waste into different types (as shown below) and provide the monthly weight of each category. Each of the waste categories has a government factor associated with it that converts kilograms of waste into kgCO2e values, which can then easily be incorporated into your footprint.

Your software may have a more extensive list of waste categories in it, but the basic ones are below[xix].

Waste type	Carbon factor (kgCO2e)
Bulk collections	0.10
Clinical waste	0.47
Confidential off-site shredding	0.03
Dry mixed recycling	0.10
Food recycling	0.15
General waste	0.47
Glass recycling	0.06
Metal recycling	0.25
Organic Household Waste	0.47
Paper and cardboard	0.08
Paper cup recycling*	1.08
WEEE (waste from electrical and electronic equipment)	0.02
Wood recycling	0.10
Waste water	0.71

*Note the high factor for paper cup recycling, demonstrating the huge potential impact of reusable travel cups and having ceramic mugs around the office.

PLASTICS

Single use plastics are a special case of waste. The carbon emissions associated with plastics is generally not significant compared to the carbon footprints of most companies, but the problems it causes for oceans and marine life mean it is worth measuring and reducing wherever possible.

It is also worth remembering that only 9% of plastic is recycled worldwide[xx], and the act of putting your drink bottles and other plastics into a green bin should not make any of us feel virtuous.

Example waste calculation

Sally runs a 100 person office in Glasgow where they have their waste split into 'general' and 'recycling'. She also has a small canteen on site.

Originally, Sally noticed that the general waste and recycled waste were being emptied into the same waste removal truck. But, having fixed the issue, both are now treated separately and food waste is picked up every day.

The waste company weighs the waste when they collect it and has given Sally a report for the past month. They picked up 5,180kg of general waste destined for landfill, 2,130kg of recycled paper and 3,900kg of food waste.

Referring to the waste carbon factors table, Sally's emissions were:

tCO2e = [tCO2e for general waste] + [tCO2e for recycled paper] + [tCO2e for food waste]

= [5180*0.47] + [2130*0.08] + [3900*0.15] kgCO2e = 3,190 kgCO2e = 3.2 tCO2e

BUSINESS TRAVEL

To determine the carbon footprint of business travel, we split it into five different categories, remembering that the fuel used in company owned vehicles has already been dealt with under Scope 1:

- Staff owned cars used for business travel
- Flights
- Trains

- Tube and taxi
- Hotel stays

We process each category separately in the normal way using carbon factors. You might also reasonably include company jets, forklift trucks, buses and so on, but in my experience, these are not so commonly used, so for clarity I have omitted them.

Top tip

The primary challenge I face when helping clients reduce their business travel footprint is that some people enjoy travelling, and they most certainly enjoy travelling in luxury when they can. Getting them to change their behaviour can sometimes be difficult, as these trips can be viewed as 'perks of the job'.

You will have more success changing or reducing the travel patterns of trips that are either repetitive or wearisome, possibly by switching those meetings across to Teams or Zoom, now that Covid-19 has normalised this style of meeting.

STAFF OWNED VEHICLES

This category is also often referred to as either 'grey fleet' or 'staff mileage', and refers to business journeys that staff make in which they use their own car and pay for the fuel themselves. In most companies, staff reclaim the costs of the fuel plus associated wear-and-tear through the expenses system. They typically record the number of miles travelled and claim a corresponding amount per mile back from the company.

Because we don't have any details of the exact amount of fuel used, we make assumptions about the average mpg of the vehicles. We can then back-calculate the amount of fuel used from the numbers of miles on the expense forms.

We group each staff vehicle into one of the following categories and use assumed mpg figures to calculate the total fuel use for each. There are others available if needed, but 99% of staff mileage typically falls into one of these major categories:

- Small diesel car with an engine size of less than 1.7 litres
- Medium diesel, 1.7-2 litres
- Large diesel, more than 2 litres

- Small petrol car with an engine size less than 1.4 litres
- Medium petrol, 1.4-2 litres
- Large petrol, more than 2 litres
- Hybrid
- Electric

If you are unsure of what size or type of vehicle a staff member used and the amount of grey fleet mileage is not significant, simply assume all cars are 'medium diesel'. If your staff mileage looks to be significant, you may need to either ask staff to record engine and fuel details in your expenses system or carry out a survey and use averages based on what you find.

The factors we use are:

Size	Measurement	Diesel	Petrol	Hybrid	Unknown	Electric
Small car	km	0.13989	0.14652	0.10332	0.1444	0.0
	miles	0.22514	0.2358	0.16628	0.23239	0.0
Medium car	km	0.168	0.1847	0.10999	0.17588	0.0
	miles	0.27039	0.29724	0.17702	0.28306	0.0
Large car	km	0.20953	0.27639	0.15491	0.22733	0.0
	miles	0.33722	0.4448	0.24929	0.36584	0.0
Average car	km	0.17082	0.17048	0.12004	0.17067	0.0
	miles	0.27492	0.27436	0.19318	0.27465	0.0
Unit: kgCo2e						

Figure 24: Carbon factors for staff mileage. Source: UK government.

Staff mileage example 1

Nell runs a kitchen, making premium sandwiches for London-based office workers.

She has a diesel company van which is used every day for deliveries, but she must occasionally pop out to the local wholesaler for ingredients. If the van is busy, she uses her privately owned Fiat Punto and claims the costs of doing this through the expenses system. Last month, she travelled 418 miles in total in the Fiat.

Her carbon emissions for staff mileage are:

418 x [carbon factor for small diesel car per mile]

= 418 x 0.22514 kgCO2e = 94 kgCO2e = 0.1 tCO2e

Staff mileage example 2

Nell then sells her Fiat Punto, fits an EV charger at her kitchen and buys an electric Smart car. Last month she reclaimed expenses for 347 miles in her new car.

Her carbon emissions for staff mileage are 0 kgCO2e, because all the electricity used to charge her car is already accounted for in her Scope 2 emissions, and to include it again would result in double-counting.

FLIGHTS

To calculate emissions involved with flights, we group them by both the type of flight and the class of seat on that flight. For the type of flight, we use the following four definitions:

- Domestic – flights that start and end in your home country
- Short-haul – short flights between countries, for example London to Berlin
- Long-haul – longer flights between continents, for example London to New York
- International – where the flight neither starts nor ends in your home country[12]

For the class of seat, we use the standard flight classes:

- Economy
- Premium Economy
- Business
- First

Each of the seat classes have different and increasing carbon factors associated with them for each type of flight.

12 I feel this category needs work and would argue that just because a flight starts and ends outside of your home country, it is still better described as a domestic, short-haul or long-haul flight.

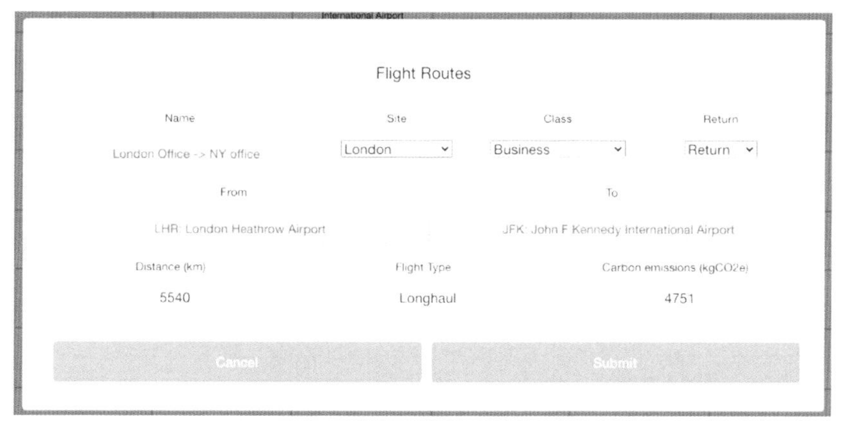

Figure 25: A typical online carbon footprint calculator for flights. This screen is from Yeti.

Fun fact

As I write this, I am sitting on an Airbus A380 plane that can carry a whopping 320,000 litres of fuel and typically uses 13,500 litres of fuel per hour. In other words, approximately four litres per second.

Different types of flight – whether domestic, short-haul or long-haul – spend differing proportions of their time ascending, descending and cruising, which all use different amounts of fuel. Seat classes also have different carbon factors – naturally, you can squeeze more passengers into economy class than business class, so the overall litres of fuel required per passenger are correspondingly different.

To calculate the carbon footprint of flights, you will therefore need to enter the following information into your software:

- Flight origin
- Flight destination
- Travel class
- Whether it was a return or one-way journey

The software will then automatically apply the corresponding carbon factor to the distance travelled (the 'great circle' distance) to calculate the overall carbon footprint of your flights.

Domestic, to/from UK	Average passenger	0.24587
Short-haul, to/from UK	Average passenger	0.15353
	Economy class	0.15102
	Business class	0.22652
Long-haul, to/from UK	Average passenger	0.19309
	Economy class	0.14787
	Premium economy class	0.23659
	Business class	0.42882
	First class	0.59147
International, to/ from non-UK	Average passenger	0.18362
	Economy class	0.140625
	Premium economy class	0.225
	Business class	0.40781
	First class	0.56251
Unit: kgCo2e per passenger km		

Figure 26: Carbon factors for flight distances. Source: UK government

Example flights carbon calculation 1

Livi works for a London-based wine retailer and travels to Bordeaux, France, four times a year to buy wine. She travels in economy class to keep costs down.

Her carbon footprint for the flights for the year will be:

4 x [distance to and from Bordeaux and back] x [carbon factor for the flight]

= 4 x [462 x 2] x [short-haul, economy]

= 4 x 462 x 2 x 0.15102 kgCO2e = 558 kgCO2e = 0.6 tCO2e

Example flights carbon calculation 2

Livi gets lucky playing the lottery and decides to fly to Napa Valley in California first class to buy some premium wines to celebrate her good fortune.

Her carbon footprint for the flights for that one flight will be:

[distance to Napa and back] x [carbon factor for the flight]

= [5354 x 2] x [long-haul, first]

= 5354 x 2 x 0.59147 = 6,333 kgCO2e = 6.3 tCO2e

Note that this one first class, long-haul flight emits approximately the same amount of carbon as 40 of her previous European, economy class flights.

HOTELS

Carbon emissions related to hotel stays vary depending on where in the world the hotel is. I've always felt that the associated carbon factors for this area (shown below) are rather simplistic, and I suspect they will get more sophisticated as better data becomes available. For example, it would be good to see smaller, eco-friendly hotels differentiated from five-star, luxury properties.

To calculate the emissions for hotel stays, multiply the number of nights spent in hotels in each location by the associated carbon factor.

Country	Unit	kgCO2e
UK	Room per night	13.9
UK (London)	Room per night	13.8
Argentina	Room per night	56
Australia	Room per night	42.6
Austria	Room per night	13.9
Belgium	Room per night	10.9
Brazil	Room per night	12.3
Canada	Room per night	16.1
Chile	Room per night	30.5
China	Room per night	62.9
Colombia	Room per night	13.5
Costa Rica	Room per night	7.5
Czech Republic	Room per night	36.2
Egypt	Room per night	56.5
Fiji	Room per night	47.8
Finland	Room per night	

Country	Unit	kgCO2e
France	Room per night	6.5
Germany	Room per night	17
Greece	Room per night	43
Hong Kong, China	Room per night	65.9
India	Room per night	75.5
Indonesia	Room per night	89.1
Ireland	Room per night	25
Israel	Room per night	54
Italy	Room per night	20.2
Japan	Room per night	60.6
Jordan	Room per night	62.4
Kazakhstan	Room per night	
Korea	Room per night	61.2
Macau, China	Room per night	75.6
Malaysia	Room per night	83
Maldives	Room per night	183.3
Mexico	Room per night	25.9
Netherlands	Room per night	20.9
New Zealand	Room per night	10.4
Oman	Room per night	
Panama	Room per night	22.1
Peru	Room per night	22.5
Philippines	Room per night	44.2
Poland	Room per night	33.2
Portugal	Room per night	26
Qatar	Room per night	126.8
Romania	Room per night	25.5
Russian Federation	Room per night	31.8
Saudi Arabia	Room per night	114.5
Singapore	Room per night	37.8
Slovak Republic	Room per night	19.1
South Africa	Room per night	61

Country	Unit	kgCO2e
Spain	Room per night	18.7
Switzerland	Room per night	7.4
Taiwan, China	Room per night	77.3
Thailand	Room per night	51
Turkey	Room per night	33.6
United Arab Emirates	Room per night	114.4
United States	Room per night	19.7
Vietnam	Room per night	51.8

Figure 27: Carbon emissions related to hotel stays throughout the world. Source: UK government

Example hotel stay carbon calculation

Whilst in Bordeaux, Livi stayed in a hotel for three nights on each of the four trips she made and stayed in a hotel for a week in Napa.

Her emissions for this were:

tCO2e = [tCO2e for Bordeaux] + [tCO2e for Napa]

= [4 x 3 x 6.5] + [1 x 7 x 19.7] kgCO2e = 216 kgCO2e = 0.2 tCO2e

TRAINS, TAXIS AND PUBLIC TRANSPORT

These are very straightforward to process if you know the distances travelled. The carbon factors to use here are shown below.

Type	kg CO2e
Regular taxi	0.14876
Black cab	0.20416
Local bus (not London)	0.10778
Local London bus	0.07936
Average local bus	0.0965
Coach	0.02733
National rail	0.03549
International rail	0.00446

Type	kg CO2e
Light rail and tram	0.02861
London Underground	0.02781
Unit: kgCO2e per passenger km	

Figure 28: Carbon factors for train, taxi and public transport. Source: UK government

However, in many cases the source of this information is the company expenses system, and whilst the amount claimed is known precisely, the distances that each claim relates to are not.

In these cases, your only option is to convert the monetary amount of expense claimed into miles travelled using average costs for the typical journeys you make. Your software will do this for you, but if you are doing it manually you can use Google Maps to calculate the averages using a representative subset of the total claims. Alternatively, you can use a Google search along the lines of "Average cost per mile for train journeys". For train journeys, the approximate costs per mile at the time of writing are:

Start	End	Cost per mile
London	Newcastle	5.5 -> 16
Bristol	Coventry	17 -> 26
Edinburgh	Glasgow	11
Cardiff	Brighton	13 -> 32
Lands End	Jon-o-Groats	12 -> 20
Unit: typical pence per mile of train journeys		

Figure 29: Typical cost per mile for train journeys in the UK. Source: Whatprice.co.uk[xxi]

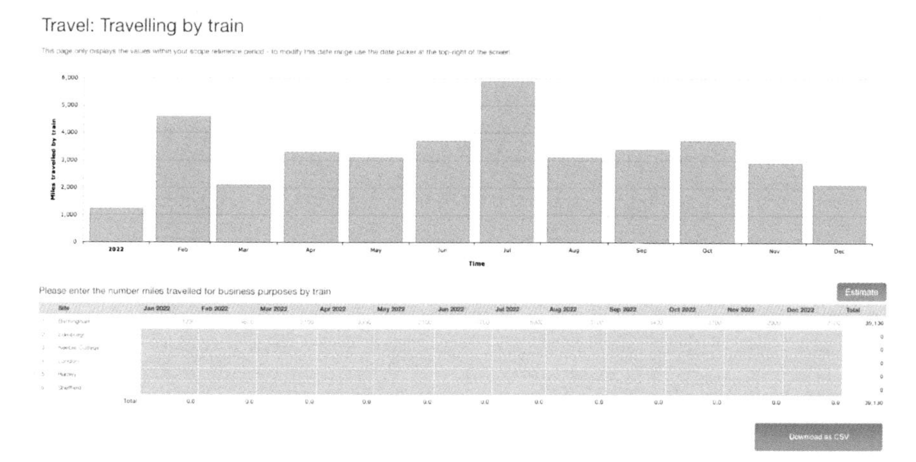

Figure 30: A typical software data entry screen for train travel. This screen is taken from Yeti.

Example rail travel carbon calculation

Alison is calculating the carbon emissions from her 17-strong sales team's rail journeys last month. Between them, they spent £4,391 on rail travel. From the table above, we will assume a cost of £0.15 per mile of rail travel.

The carbon footprint for these journeys would be:

[distance travelled by train] x [carbon factor for National Rail journeys]

= [4391 / 0.15] x 0.03549 kgCO_2e = 29,273 x 0.03549 = 1,038 kgCO_2e = 1.0 tCO_2e

COMMUTING

A staff survey is an efficient way of gathering data on staff commuting. Your software should have a survey function built in, but if not, you can manually create a survey to ask staff the following questions:

- What mode of transport do you use to get into and out of work (car, bike, walk, bus, train or a mix of these)?
- How far is each leg of your journey?
- If you drive, what category of car do you use (small petrol, large diesel, electric, etc.)?
- How many times a week do you commute?

- How many days a week do your work from home?

Typically, you are unlikely to receive a high response rate to the survey, and you are doing well with a rate of 30%. In my experience, 85% would be exceptionally high, but 10% would be unsurprising. Your software will then scale this sample set up to be representative of your entire staff base, or you can do it manually.

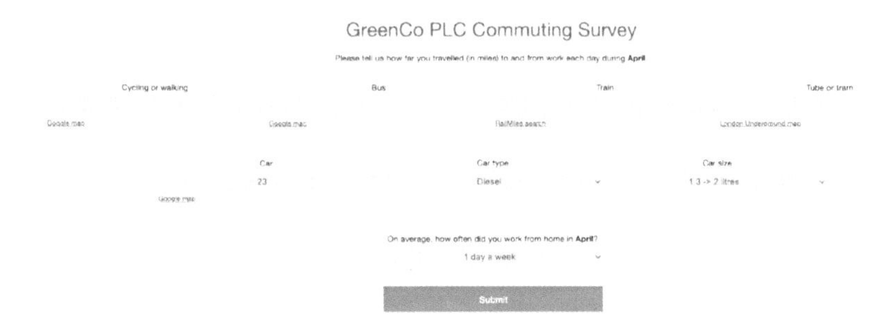

Figure 31: A typical online survey to determine commuting patterns across your staff base.

Once you have the input data, you can use the same analysis techniques shown for business travel (see above) to determine your commuting footprint.

Example commuting carbon calculation

Beth has been asked to work out the commuting carbon footprint for her 25 colleagues. Because of the wide range of possible permutations, this calculation is not one she wanted to do manually, so she sets up an online survey in her carbon management platform and gets the following results:

Staff commuting footprint = 17 tCO_2e per annum

WORKING FROM HOME

When we ran a work from home analysis for one of Enistic's larger clients during the Covid-19 pandemic, we were all expecting to see significantly fewer carbon emissions when working from home because of the savings associated with not commuting. Interestingly, what we found is that the carbon emissions associated with the additional heating of staff member's homes were more significant than we had anticipated.

Later, when the UK government subsequently released the official carbon factors for working from home, our analysis was confirmed and the savings our client was expecting to see weren't there. Broadly speaking, they only saw a 30% saving from their staff working from home rather than in the office, which surprised us.

To calculate your work from home emissions, multiply the number of days staff worked from home (obtained from the commuting survey) by the working from home carbon factor. This carbon factor accounts for things like heating, lighting, preparing hot drinks, and so on.

Activity	kgCO2e
Office Equipment	0.25343327
Heating	2.47259325
Homeworking (office equipment + heating)	2.72602652

Figure 32: Carbon factors for working from home. Source: UK government

Example work from home carbon calculation

Sally's company has embraced the modern way of working and gone 100% remote. They have relinquished their offices in Aberdeen and now all 212 employees work from home for 48 weeks a year, five days per week. She has been asked to calculate the associated carbon footprint of this new way of working.

tCO2e = [number of days worked from home] x [work from home carbon factor]

= [212 x 48 x 5] x 2.73 kgCO2e = 138,902 kgCO2e = 139 tCO2e

HOW TO COMMUNICATE YOUR FOOTPRINT WITHOUT MISLEADING PEOPLE

Once you input all relevant data into the software and it has calculated your overall carbon footprint, how do you then go about communicating the result to your stakeholders? Care is needed here, and there's a common pitfall to avoid.

If you say to people, *"After much work, we now know our carbon footprint was 323 tCO2e last year"*, they will just remember the figure of '323 tCO2e last year'. You *must* tell them standard you have used and whether there were any problems with or gaps in the data (as there generally are, particularly when it comes to obtaining accurate supply chain emissions data).

A better way to communicate your carbon footprint would be:

> *"We don't know precisely what our carbon footprint is yet, as the data for our supply chain emissions is far from complete. However, our certified Net Zero footprint was 323 tCO2e last year, and we will have a more precise figure when we repeat the process next year using more accurate supplier data."*

This may feel like overkill, but often the base data you have used to calculate your footprint will change from year to year. And, unless senior management are aware that it is likely to change, you are likely to face uncomfortable questions in subsequent years.

WHAT TO DO IF THE DATA OR CARBON FACTORS CHANGE

With carbon accounting in its infancy, carbon footprint data from your suppliers is likely to change. Furthermore, as official calculations are reworked, carbon factors occasionally change too. Through no fault of your own, the footprint you calculated last year may be completely different if you calculated it again knowing what you know now. Comparing the carbon footprint across different years therefore needs careful consideration.

The best way to tackle the problem is to recalculate previous years using new factors and explain clearly why things have changed. Make sure to state what the figures were before and after they were recalculated, so people can see how much the changes in the base data have impacted your results.

The fact that your carbon footprint could (likely will) change when it is recalculated is something some people will have difficulty wrapping their heads around. Accountants are used to precise figures that don't change, and your explanation for why they have changed may fall on deaf ears. It is therefore important to always qualify your carbon footprint: *"With what we know today, it is [X tCO2e]. However, our understanding of the issue, and the associated data, continues to change over time."*

"On an increasingly crowded planet, humanity faces many threats - but none is greater than climate change. It magnifies every hazard and tension of our existence."

King Charles III

Chapter 8

SETTING AN AMBITIOUS CARBON REDUCTION TARGET

Carbon Reduction Plan Section Three

If you are on the Net Zero journey, you must set targets, not only because it is good practice, but because it is a requirement of PPN 06/21. Targets give you something to aim for: they allow you to judge whether the plans you made to reduce your carbon emissions are working, and whether the overall reductions achieved are meaningful.

Targets are normally represented by a reduction of X% by year Y compared to year Z. For example: *"Compared to our carbon emissions in financial year ending 2023, we will...*

- *"...reduce our carbon emissions by 50% by 2030"*; or
- *"...achieve Net Zero by 2025"*; or
- *"...achieve Net Zero by 2027 and reduce our carbon emissions by 95% by 2045"*; or
- *"...reduce our Scope 1 and Scope 2 emissions to zero by 2026"*.

You might choose targets based on multiple dates, such as:

- *"Compared to 2023, we will reduce our Scope 1 and Scope 2 emissions by 95% by 2027 and our overall carbon footprint by 95% by 2045"*.

And they don't need to be based on absolute numbers – relative measures are also valid:

- *"Compared to 2023, we will reduce the amount of carbon in each of the cups we manufacture by 45% by 2028"*[13].

Whatever you choose, there are a few rules you should follow:

- Your targets must be ambitious.
- You must state the year to which you will compare your reduction targets (2023 in the example above), known as the 'reference year' or 'base year'.
- You must achieve Net Zero by 2050 in line with PPN 06/21 requirements.

CHOOSING THE CORRECT REFERENCE YEAR

When you come to choose a reference year, there are a couple of factors you ought to bear in mind. Firstly, with Covid-19 affecting so many aspects of so many businesses, be careful to not choose a year heavily affected by lockdowns as your base year. Your carbon emissions that year are not likely to be representative of a typical year and, often, are going to be significantly lower than they otherwise might have been. If you select one of these low carbon years as your reference year, it is likely that your carbon will go up in subsequent years even if you work hard to reduce it, because of your increased activity levels. This won't be because your carbon reduction projects are failing, it will be because your reference year was artificially low and any comparisons against it are always going to look bad.

Secondly, on a similar note, the further back you go, the larger your carbon footprint will typically be. All future comparisons against an earlier starting point will therefore look better than if you choose a more recent, lower carbon year[14].

Finally – and this one is the clincher for most – you will need the full set of data to calculate the carbon footprint of your chosen reference year. Your record keeping and time availability may be better than most, but the vast majority of companies don't have the time, inclination, or data to choose any reference year except for the current one.

13 This is an example of a *carbon intensity* and is useful if your company changes the size and shape of its operations from year to year.

14 I have seen one large company state that, *"Compared to 2008, our carbon emissions have reduced by …"*. That may be true but highlighting their more recent progress would give a more accurate picture of the results of their carbon reduction efforts.

MAKE YOUR TARGET AMBITIOUS

What ambitious looks like for you will very much depend on your own circumstances, but the planet is getting dangerously hot and our objective is to do our part in limiting this warming. Reducing your carbon emissions by 5% over 30 years is not going to cut it, so think ambitiously – *"Aim for the stars and hit the moon"*.

DIFFERENT TYPES OF TARGETS

As we have seen, there are several different ways we can define our reduction targets. The two most common are *absolute reductions* and *intensity reductions*.

ABSOLUTE REDUCTION TARGETS

The first and easiest type of target is an absolute reduction in your overall carbon footprint with reference to a base year. For example, *"Compared with 2018, we are going to reduce our carbon emissions by 45% by 2030"*.

I like these targets because they are simple to measure and transparent. They do not cope well, however, with fast-changing companies. For example, if your company head count doubles, it is likely your carbon footprint will increase proportionally, as it would if you manufactured 200% more widgets this year than last year. In such cases, it would be better to use an intensity target rather than an absolute target.

INTENSITY REDUCTION TARGETS

Recognising the changing nature of companies, particularly small and medium sized companies, another target you can choose is a reduction in your carbon intensity – in other words, a reduction in the amount of carbon emitted per unit produced. For example:

- *"By 2030, we're going to reduce our carbon emissions per client by 45% compared to 2023"*
- *"Compared to 2023, we're going to reduce our carbon emissions per £1,000 of profit by 70% by 2027"*

- *"Compared to 2023, we're going to reduce our carbon emissions per guest per night in our hotel by 50% by 2029"*

Intensity reduction targets are popular because they allow for company size changes, and intensity targets based on kgCO2e per £1,000 of profit generated are becoming increasingly popular.

If you are in the manufacturing, construction or agriculture sector you would be wise to adopt an intensity reduction target rather than an absolute reduction target.

Carbon intensities are discussed in more detail in Chapter 10.

NEAR-TERM AND LONG-TERM TARGETS

You can, should you wish, have more than one target, and this is common among those who follow Science Based Targets, which stipulates that you must have two different goals.

One target might be near-term, looking perhaps 5-10 years into the future. This is, to be frank, the one that people find most realistic. This might then be accompanied by a longer-term target; for example, *'Net Zero by 2050'*. I have yet to find anyone that truly believes in their plans to achieve their long-term targets, but standards such as PPN 06/21 require you to have one. Adopting a long-term target of *'Net Zero by 2050'* and focussing your attention on your short-term plans could therefore be a wise approach.

SCIENCE BASED TARGETS: LINKING TARGETS TO CLIMATE CHANGE

Two organisations doing fantastic work to help individuals and businesses through the maze of climate change and its impact upon the planet are the United Nations and the Science Based Targets initiative (SBTi).

Periodically, the SBTi reviews changes in global temperatures, the amount of carbon we're putting into the atmosphere and the amount we are removing. They model the long-term effects of this and advise what companies need to reduce their carbon emissions by to keep the global temperature increase under 1.5 °C; or more realistically, under 2°C. At the time of writing, these reduction targets are set at a minimum of 4.2% year-on-year reductions.

If you have a larger company, you might consider the SBTi's targets to be the natural choice for your Carbon Reduction Plan. For small and medium sized companies, however, although it is worthwhile following SBTi guidance, the additional work required to reformulate reduction plans each year is quite a burden. Most SMEs will use the simpler targets shown above. Hopefully, future software iterations will make it easier for smaller and medium-sized companies to adopt SBTi targets.

Chapter 9

REDUCING YOUR CARBON EMISSIONS

Carbon Reduction Plan Section Four

Measuring your carbon footprint and setting targets is all well and good, but the real reason we're here is to reduce our footprint. This chapter is focussed on tangible actions you can take to begin meaningfully reducing your carbon emissions.

HOW TO PRIORITISE YOUR CARBON REDUCTION PROJECTS

Most software systems will have an extensive range of possible carbon reduction projects built in. To help you decide which to undertake, I recommend you first select those most obvious to you and your business and then categorise the rest by giving each a rating to reflect both its cost and likely payback time (how long a project takes to pay for itself). I recommend a letter and number system (A1, C3, B1, B2 and so on) in which the letter represents the cost and the number represents the payback time.

RATING BY COST

Give each potential project a cost rating of A, B or C, where A is the cheapest, C is the most expensive and B is everything in-between. What you classify as cheap and expensive is highly subjective and completely up to you. Only you know your budgets, and what one company might consider expensive another might consider cheap, and vice versa.

You might, for example, decide that:

- A = anything we can easily do using existing budget allocations
- B = neither especially cheap or particularly expensive, to be considered on a case-by-case basis
- C = significantly more budget would need to be allocated to us if we wanted to do it

Alternatively:

- A = under £5,000
- B = between £5,000 and £50,000
- C = over £50,000

RATING BY PAYBACK TIME

If a project costs £10,000 and you save £1,000 a year as a result of the project, you have a payback time of 10 years. You can rank payback times as 1, 2 or 3, where 1 is fast, 3 is slow and 2 is everything in-between.

Alternatively, you could conduct more in-depth lifecycle analysis (LCA) to look not only at the purchase cost, but also the differences in operating, maintenance, installation and disposal costs. This analysis is probably worth doing before you make larger investments, but in most cases a simple payback calculation is sufficient.

SELECTION OF PROJECTS

Once you have classified all of the projects relevant to you, common sense will often help you choose which to implement and when. However, if you get stuck deciding you could put your projects into a prioritisation grid, as shown in the example below.

Along the bottom row you have cost, and in the left column is payback time. The coloured boxes are labelled according to when you might consider implementing the project.

Fast payback time	Year 2	Year 1	Now
Medium payback time	Year 3	Year 2	Year 1
Slow payback time	Never	Year 3	Year 2
	C - Expensive	B - Mid-priced	A - Cheap

Figure 33: Example carbon reduction project prioritisation grid.

A QUICK ENERGY QUIZ TO GET YOU STARTED

Take the following quiz to assess your company's energy use, with a maximum score of 24 points.

ENERGY MANAGEMENT MATRIX

Your Score	Maximum Score
	24

Score	Policy	Organising	Training	Performance measurement	Communication	Investment
0	No explicit energy policy	No delegation of responsibility for managing energy	No energy-related staff training undertaken	No measurement of energy costs or consumption	No communication or promotion of energy-related issues	No investment in improving energy efficiency
1	An unwritten set of guidelines	Informal mostly focused on short-term gains	Technical staff occasionally attend specialist courses	invoice checking only	Ad-hoc informal contacts used to promote energy efficiency	Only low or no-cost measures taken
2	Un-adopted policy	Some delegation of responsibility but line management and authority unclear	Ad-hoc internal training for selected people as requested	Monthly monitoring by fuel type	Some use of company communication mechanisms to promote energy efficiency	Low or medium cost measures are considered if the short payback
3	Formal policy but no active commitment from top management	Clear line management accountability for consumption and responsibility for improvement	Energy training targeted at major users following a training needs analysis	Weekly performance measurement for each process, unit, or building	Regular staff briefings, performance reporting and energy promotion	Some appraisal criteria used for other cost-reduction projects
4	Energy Policy, Action Plan and regular review have the active commitment of top management	Fully integrated into management structure with clear accountability for energy consumption	Appropriate and comprehensive staff training tailored to identified needs, with evaluation	Comprehensive performance measurement against targets with effective management reporting	Extensive communication of energy issues within and outside of the organisation	Resources routinely committed to energy efficiency in support of business objectives

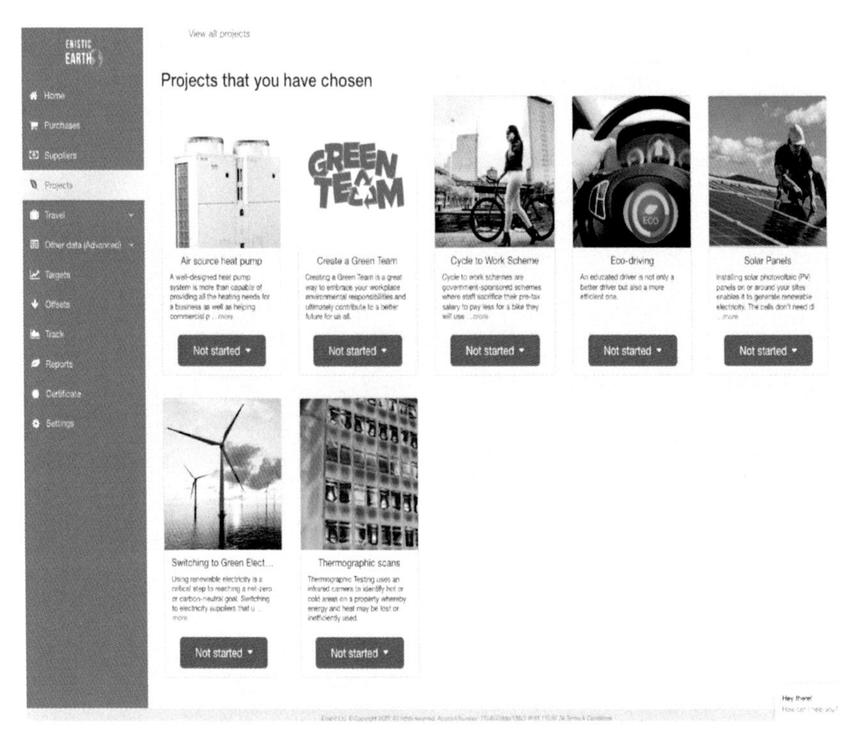

Figure 41: A typical project selection and customisation section from an online system. This is taken from Yeti.

In the future we hope to implement further measures such as:

Strategic review

In 2022, we initiated a process to regularly review the impact our business is having on the environment, and the progress of our carbon reduction projects. We review our emissions data on a monthly basis to determine any opportunities for improvement in reducing consumption and increasing efficiency. Furthermore, we will be setting up an ESG Steering Group, chaired by our MD, that will hold quarterly review meetings on our sustainability goals and provide suggestions to our board for improvement.

Working with our supply chain

Transitioning to a low carbon business model cannot be achieved without the help of our suppliers. Our supply chain contributes significantly to our scope 3 footprint. Hence, we aim to work with our suppliers to implement environmental management systems across their operations. In addition to that we will be creating a system to which our suppliers could report their emissions data which will inform possible savings opportunities.

Fleet electrification

Nearly 60% of our total Scope 1 & 2 emissions are created by emissions from our company vehicles. This provides us with an excellent opportunity to reduce emissions by electrifying our road fleet. In 2022, 66% of new company vehicles ordered were electric, with a trial of electric vans underway. This would enable us to reduce a significant amount of our emissions and also future-proof our business against the effects of anthropogenic climate change.

Increasing building efficiency

Increasing the energy efficiency of our buildings will be a priority as we move towards our net zero goal. With the help of Enistic, we ensure that we are compliant with the UK government's Energy Savings Opportunity Scheme (ESOS). But with a view to going above and beyond, we aim to implement the following measures.

- On-site energy generation using solar to ensure energy security
- Purchase renewable electricity for all our buildings
- Switch to LED lighting
- Conduct workshops for staff which train them on sustainable work practices

Figure 34: A typical projects section in a Carbon Reduction Plan. This page was taken from Yeti

PROJECT 1: BASELOAD ANALYSIS

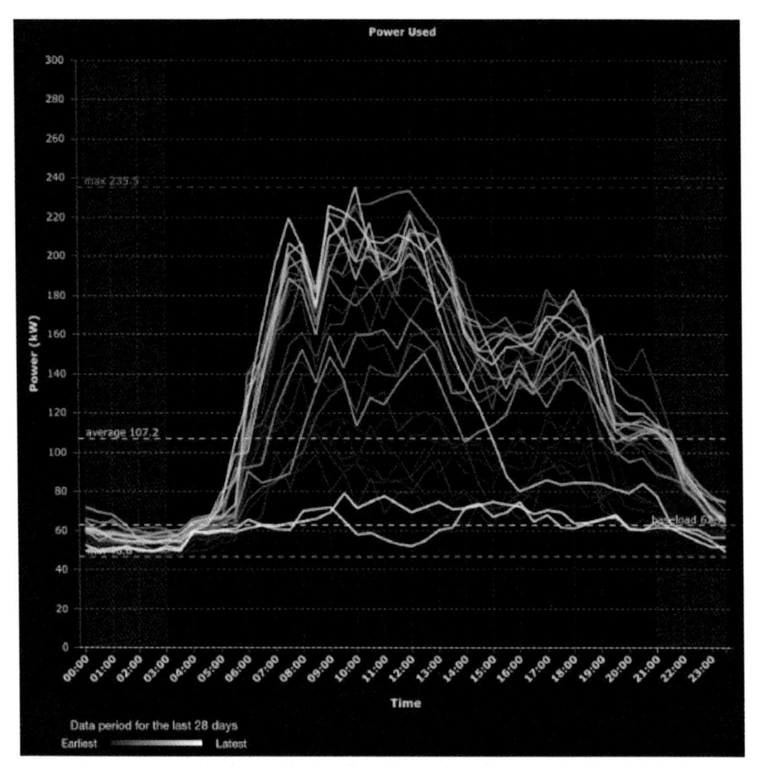

Figure 35: 2D view of a typical baseload analysis. Note that the power being used rarely drops below 90kW

'Baseload analysis' may sound complicated, but all you're actually doing here is assessing what is being left on unnecessarily at night and on weekends on your business sites.

To do this properly, a smart meter is needed. If you do not already have one, contact your utilities provider to get one fitted (at a cost of approximately £700 at the time of writing). Your software should then be able to connect to the smart meter to download your power readings for the past month at 30-minute intervals. These can then be used to visualise your usage on a 2D graph like the one shown above, or in 3D as shown below.

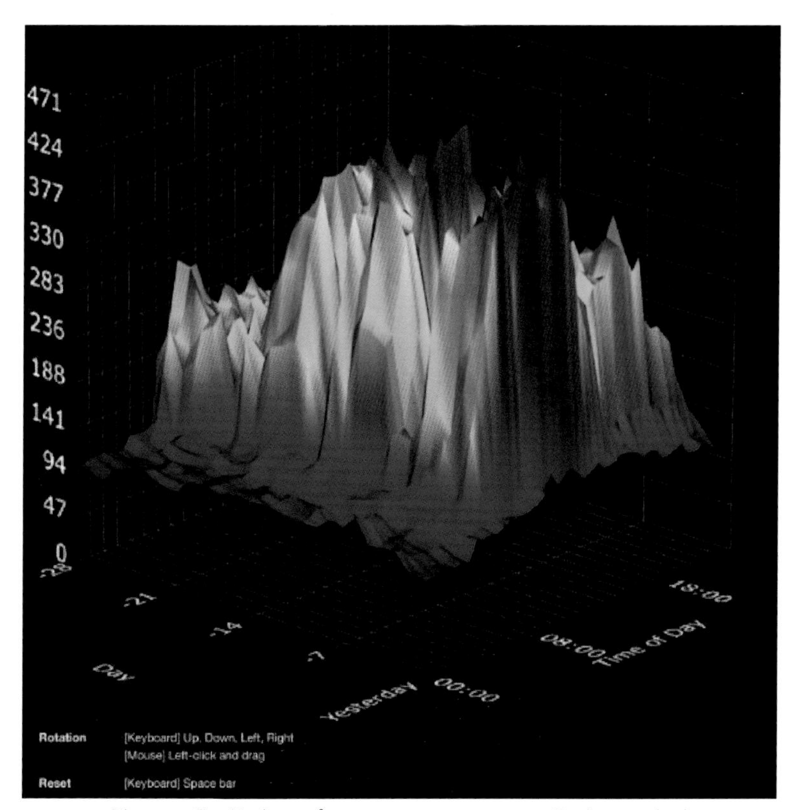

Figure 36: *3D view of power usage over a 28-day period.*

On the 3D graph (Fig 36), the X-axis shows days, typically covering the past month, with each left to right slice representing one day. On the Z-axis (at 90 degrees to the X-axis) you have the time of day, from 00:00 through to 23:30; and on the Y-axis is the power usage. The IT team at my office love these graphs because they look impressive, especially as they can be spun around and zoomed in and out. Our carbon consultants prefer the 2D version in which each trace represents a day and historical data is represented by fading lines.

The graphs help to identify the power that your business sites are using during the night when, in theory at least, nearly everything should be turned off – aside from the fire alarm, burglar alarm, phone system and so on. These things use almost no power, and in a well-run office that doesn't have servers or other machines running 24/7 (as opposed to a manufacturing facility in which machines are intentionally running all hours), the power being used at 3am should be minimal and typically in the region of 1-3kW.

However, most companies use far more power than they should, and the graphs shown above are real examples from one of my clients. It turns out that this client had air conditioning systems, pumps and fans running 24/7 that should have been switched off but weren't. In some cases, this was due to poor control systems[15], in others, people had simply got out of the habit of switching things off at night. The costs of running this equipment 24/7 can be significant, and in the above case, savings of over £100,000 were identified, resulting in a carbon reduction of 65 tCO_2e per year.

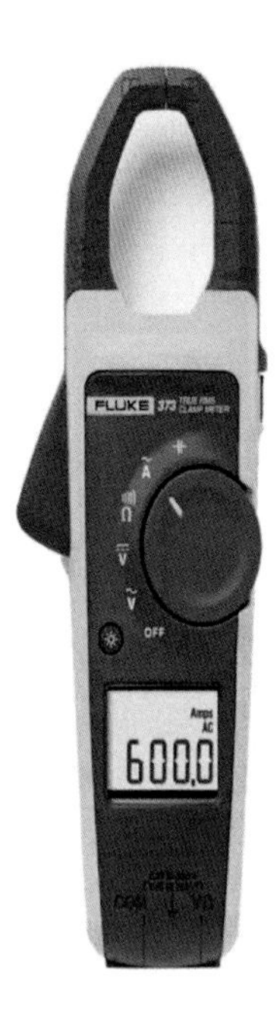

Figure 37: A clip-on power meter used by an electrician to identify equipment that has been left running at night. Photo credit: Fluke.

If you think that you might have a problem with equipment running when it shouldn't be, the simplest method to find out what is causing the problem is to either:

- concentrate on turning things off manually in the evening and checking if it has solved the problem the next morning; or
- failing that, ask your electrician to buy a clip-on power meter and either early one morning or late one night when things should be turned off,

15 When new equipment is installed, those installing it are often more interested in avoiding technical issues than they are about energy consumption. As such, most installers will configure equipment to run for longer periods of time than it needs to, often leaving things to run 24/7.

go through the electrical distribution boards and track down what is still running. In my experience, it is nearly always fans or pumps.

Whichever method you use, the effort required to sort these problems out is far outweighed by the savings you can make.

A bad case of overnight use

I did a baseload analysis for a company in Toronto, where they had an unusually high baseload and couldn't figure out why.

It turned out that when the building was first commissioned, the person who specified it had 'a thing' about not having snow on the pathways around the building. He had a heating system installed under the pavements that was turned on when the building was first commissioned many years ago, but no one ever got around to turning it off.

One of the staff there said to me, *"We always wondered why the pavements around our building never got snowy"*.

PROJECT 2: IMPROVE YOUR INSULATION

If you plan to heat or cool your building, it is worth spending some time checking your insulation. You can do this using a thermographic camera or, in the first instance, by simply checking the amount of energy you use in summer compared to what you use in winter. In a well-insulated building, it should not make a lot of difference what the outside temperature is, whereas in a poorly insulated building, your heating system will be working overtime to provide heat to the inside space which then quickly dissipates through the walls and ceilings.

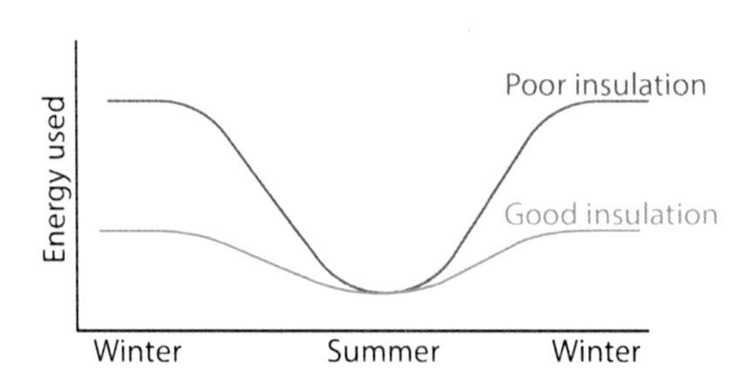

Figure 38: Poorly insulated buildings require significantly more energy to heat in cold weather.

A bad case of poor insulation

A company in Nottingham had a warehouse to store large rolls of steel that would be put onto the back of HGV lorries and shipped to whoever needed them. The steel could not be allowed to rust, so they heated the warehouse to prevent dew forming on it using three large furnaces that each burnt diesel and blew heated air out into the warehouse.

To make it quicker for the HGVs to come and go, the warehouse had floor to ceiling holes in three of the four walls, each with the dimensions of the back of an HGV. The HGVs would back into these holes to be loaded up three or four times per day, leaving the huge holes open to the outside when they weren't there. There were no roller shutters, no doors and no air curtains, just these massive holes in the walls.

As you might imagine, the three furnaces did little except heat the air which quickly escaped through the holes, especially if there was anything more than a mild breeze blowing. The winter fuel bill for the warehouse was £83,000 *per month more* than their summer fuel bill.

The company in question has since gone out of business.

The second, more technical way of checking your insulation levels is using an infrared camera. You can hire someone to do a scan of your building, or if you would rather do it yourself the cameras are readily available online starting at £400 each.

To carry out a thermographic scan, choose a cold night without much breeze or rain and turn the heating on inside the building. After the inside has warmed up, point the camera at the outside of the building. You should be able to see very quickly which parts of the building are well insulated (appearing blue in most systems) and which are poorly insulated (red or pink).

Figure 39: Thermographic scan of a building showing where heat escapes as a result of poor insulation. Photo credit: Infratek.

PROJECT 3: FIX THE DRAUGHTS

A lower-tech solution, the next thing to look at is similar to insulation: draughts. Draughts are cheap and simple to fix, and you will typically save significantly more than you spend.

Draught excluding foam is a material commonly used to seal gaps and cracks around windows and doors, effectively preventing cold air from entering a room and warm air from escaping. This material is usually made of a soft, flexible foam that can be easily compressed to fit into narrow spaces. By blocking these gaps, draught excluding foam can help to maintain a comfortable temperature within a room while reducing the workload on your heating and cooling systems, ultimately leading to lower energy bills. Additionally, draught excluding foam can also help to reduce noise pollution and prevent the entry of dust, insects, and other small particles, making it a useful and versatile material for maintaining a comfortable and healthy indoor environment.

Figure 40: *Draught excluding foam.*

You might also consider the inrush of cold air that occurs on doors that open to the outside. Last month, I was in a building reception area that was very warm until the outside was opened, at which point the cold air rushed in. The receptionist told me that, as a result, under his desk he had a portable electric fan heater that was constantly on.

There are a few ways of resolving this problem:

1. Install a double door to the outside by constructing a porch, effectively creating a basic air lock; or
2. Install a revolving door; or
3. Fit an air curtain to provide a constant stream of heated air. This may seem like a counter-intuitive way to save money, but the invisible barrier that the air curtain forms keeps the hot and cold air from mixing, hence reducing your heating costs.

PROJECT 4: FLOOD FIT LED LIGHTING

It's almost impossible these days to buy lighting which *isn't* LED, but if you still have fluorescent tubes in your buildings, it's time to take those out. LED lighting gives you a better quality of light, lasts longer and uses a fraction of the energy of traditional lighting systems. A typical GU10 style halogen spot-lamp, for example, will use 40 watts (W), whereas the LED equivalent will consume just 4W[16].

Most of my clients have a 'break-fix-replace' policy, whereby lamps are replaced with the LED equivalents when they stop working. However, I would urge you to set aside some time and budget to replace all your old-style lighting with LED lighting, not just the bulbs that have blown. In most cases, the payback period for the new lights is quick, and in virtually all cases the carbon saving from the new lights is considerable.

---

16 I analysed a primary school in Oxfordshire recently where they had just fitted a new lighting system comprised of the cheapest possible lights they could find from their approved suppliers. This turned out to be a T12 system, which were all the rage in the 1960's. It saddened me to think that the local council didn't have the foresight to fund LED lighting instead, which would have saved a fortune in running costs in the medium to long term, and resulted in significant carbon savings.

Sneaky tricks in cheap LED lighting panels

Lots of modern offices use ceiling light panels that are 60x60cm, the same size as ceiling tiles. Often, they contain four two-foot fluorescent tubes that can be replaced by a single LED panel of the same size and shape. The price of these units varies considerably.

Wanting to understand the price difference, we analysed a cheap LED panel versus an expensive panel.

All LEDs dim over time, and we found that the cheaper panels dimmed faster than the expensive ones, partly because the LEDs on the expensive panels had a better-designed cooling system. We discovered that the time for the LED panel to dim to 70% of its original brightness is quoted in the specification and is called the 'L70' time, where a long L70 time is better.

To get around the dimming problem, some of the cheap panels had a timer fitted that slowly increased the power to the LEDs over time. This caused them to run hotter and hotter to maintain their brightness, consuming more power as they did so which somewhat defeats the object.

Before you purchase any, take a careful look at the ratings of LED panels, particularly what we now know of as the L70 rating.

PROJECT 5: SIZING YOUR CAPACITY ALLOCATION

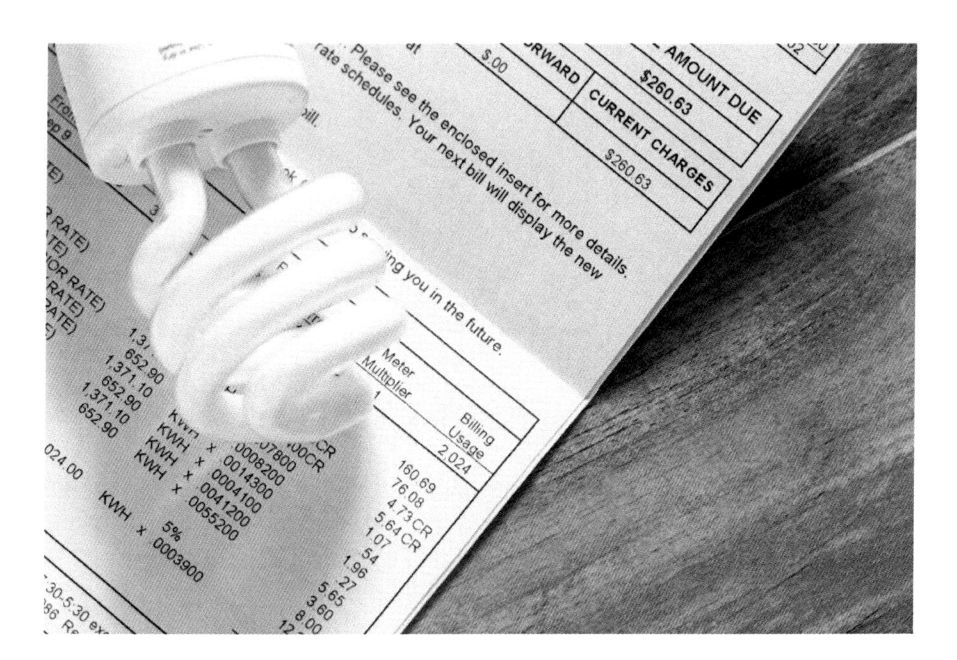

This one isn't really a carbon saving project, as it only really saves money. Nevertheless, I have included it in case it is of interest.

When a company signs up for a new energy contract, there is the expectation that when someone turns on the switch in the morning, the lights come on. In other words, they expect there to be enough energy available to meet their needs[17]. To help energy providers plan, they ask you for the maximum amount of power you are ever going to need, and then guarantee that you will always have at least that amount of power available.

When they initially set up these supply guarantees: (a) it was typically many years ago, and since then your equipment is likely to have become far more energy-efficient; and (b) they always play it safe and set the guarantees significantly above the level you will ever need. The energy company will charge you in proportion to the amount of power they guarantee, so if the guaranteed amount of power is high, your costs will also be high.

17 To make sure everyone has enough energy minute-to-minute, National Grid headquarters has a hotline to many 'quick' and 'ultra-quick' energy sources that can be turned on and off as needed in seconds, such as standby generators or pumped-high water reservoirs. These work well, but are expensive to use.

If you have a smart meter fitted to monitor your energy usage, you should be able to reduce your guaranteed power amount and, in turn, your electricity charges. Look for the 'capacity charge' or 'kVA charge' (which stands for kilovolt amperes) on your bill, and if you don't know how to optimise it yourself, reach out to either an energy expert or the utility company to see if it can be safely reduced.

Capacity charge savings in a New Zealand hardware store

One of our clients was a hardware store in New Zealand, a 'big-shed retailer'. On the roof of their building were two air conditioning units used for heating and cooling the store. Every morning (including days when the store was shut!), their building management system would turn both systems on at exactly 07.30.

When they were first turned on, the motors in the air conditioning system drew a lot of power for a very short amount of time (a 'spike') as the motors spun up from rest. As they both came on at exactly the same time, the maximum power these two units took was the sum of these two spikes, and their capacity charge had been set to accommodate this extremely short, double spike.

Using a cheap and simple delay-unit, we set one air conditioning unit to start up five minutes after the other. The start-up power spikes still occurred, but at different times, and not one on top of the other. This halved the size of the largest power spike, allowing us to halve the amount of power we were guaranteed and hence halve associated costs of the capacity charge.

The retailer saved approximately £35,000 per year as a result of this simple change.

PROJECT 6: SAFED TRAINING

SAFED stands for 'Safe and Fuel-Efficient Driver' training. It can help to reduce fuel consumption and costs by teaching drivers techniques like eco-driving, which involves maintaining a steady speed, avoiding hard acceleration and braking, and anticipating traffic flow. These techniques not only save fuel, but also reduce wear and tear on vehicles, leading to lower maintenance costs.

Safe driving practices can also reduce the risk of accidents and associated costs such as insurance claims, legal fees and vehicle repairs. Driver training can teach drivers how to identify and avoid potential hazards, maintain a safe following distance and handle adverse weather conditions.

Investing in driver training can improve staff morale and retention by demonstrating a commitment to employee safety and wellbeing. By providing training that enhances driver skills and knowledge, companies can help their employees feel more valued and motivated, leading to higher job satisfaction and reduced staff turnover.

Typically, SAFED courses are delivered online, and you should not only include them in your staff induction program, but also repeat them annually to maintain skills. Payback times will vary depending on factors such as the size of the company, the number of drivers and existing driving practices, but studies have shown that companies can typically recoup their investment in driver training within a relatively short timeframe.

A study by the UK government's Energy Saving Trust found that companies can achieve fuel savings of up to 15% through eco-driving techniques, which can lead to payback times of less than six months and overall, fuel-efficient driver training is likely to be a sound investment for small companies looking to reduce costs and improve staff morale.

PROJECT 7: FIT A BUILDING MANAGEMENT SYSTEM

I once spoke with an electrical engineer who was fitting a building management system to a pub. He remarked that a computerised controller which checked the temperature 20 times per second and determined the most efficient way to increase or reduce the temperature in the pub did a much better job than Steve, who worked behind the bar and turned it up a notch if it felt a bit chilly. Wise words indeed.

'Building management system' is a term with a wide definition. It can range from having a plug-in timer on some pieces of equipment, through to a control system that automates the entire running of the building for you. They vary widely in terms of cost, function and complexity. Some are plug-and-play whilst others require complicated programming and configuration, and modern systems monitor how the building is used to learn themselves how best to optimise building functions[18].

One of the most basic functions of a building management system is to maintain the temperature at a comfortable level; but that raises the question, what temperature should that be? Instead of setting a simple temperature level, say 21°C, try setting an upper and lower band. If you set a minimum and maximum temperature, say 19°C to 23°C, you can fire

18 In practice, I've rarely seen these self-learning systems perform well, though I suspect they will improve as time goes on.

the heating system for longer periods before it cuts off, and leave longer between cycles, both of which are more efficient than frequent on/off cycles.

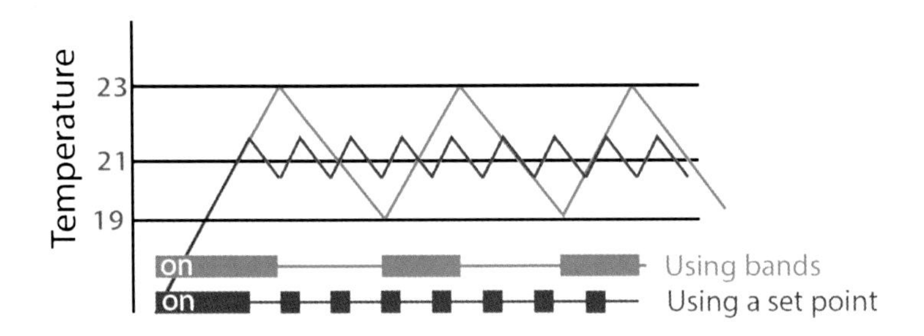

Figure 42: Setting a temperature band rather than an absolute temperature saves energy. The wider the band, the more energy you will save. The solid blocks show when the boiler is 'firing', i.e. burning gas.

Another energy saving aspect to consider is switching off the heating system one hour before lunch and then again for one hour before your employees go home. You might find that the residual temperature in your workplace means that staff do not notice the temperature start to drop, and yet, assuming an eight-hour working day, you may have just cut your heating costs by 25%.

A bad case of poor building management

We did some analysis on the energy consumption of a high-profile media company's building in Toronto, which they suspected was higher than it should be.

Whoever programmed the building management system had not put in any form of checks about whether the air conditioning system was working correctly, and when one of the units malfunctioned the system did not pick this up.

One of the large air handling units on the roof had malfunctioned and was stuck permanently on heating mode, ignoring the commands to swap over to cooling mode in the summer. The net result was that during the winter everything was fine, but in summer the units fought each other, with one heating the internal space and one cooling it, causing excessive energy consumption.

PROJECT 8: ENERGY AUDITS AND SUB-METERS

One of the problems associated with reducing your carbon emissions and energy use is knowing just how good or bad things are at the start of the process, so you can track how far you've come. You can address part of this problem by conducting an energy audit.

The simplest forms of energy audit involve walking around your building and making a record of everything using power. Then, either estimates are made or sub-meters (which monitor one specific piece of equipment or electrical circuit) are fitted to determine what equipment is inefficient. Finally, calculations are performed to work out how much would be saved if that equipment were upgraded or replaced.

As well as cost-savings, an energy audit can provide:

- **Increased energy efficiency** – by identifying areas of energy waste, an energy audit can help businesses implement energy-efficient measures that reduce their energy consumption and carbon footprint.
- **Improved comfort and productivity** – energy audits can also identify areas where improvements to building systems, such as lighting and heating, can improve occupant comfort and productivity.

- **Compliance** - energy audits can help businesses comply with regulations and standards related to energy efficiency and carbon emissions.
- **Long-term savings** - they can help businesses plan for long-term energy savings by identifying energy-efficient upgrades that can be made over time.

If you have a manufacturing site, energy audits and sub-meters can be very useful to identify incorrect and energy inefficient manners of operating equipment. If you leave them installed for long enough to spot trends, they are also an excellent way of seeing what equipment could benefit from pre-emptive maintenance.

PROJECT 9: CHILLERS AND OTHER TIME-INSENSITIVE PROCESSES

If you've got an energy-intensive process that is not time-sensitive, an easy way to save money may be to consider running your equipment at times when energy is cheapest. The most expensive time of day for energy consumption is early evening, when people come home and start preparing their dinners.

Of course, this only works for certain types of energy loads. A hospital, for example, cannot turn off important equipment when energy prices are high, but some equipment operations are not as time critical as you might think. A good example of this are commercial chillers and cold stores. During cheaper energy times, a cold store can be chilled sufficiently to see it through the high energy cost times, thus avoiding peak energy prices.

Scheduling energy use in UK supermarkets

A major UK supermarket has a device fitted to the control systems of their (many) in-store freezers.

It monitors the temperature of each chiller and the energy price every 30 minutes. The system has built in protections to avoid food spoiling, but attempts to make the best use of cheaper energy to run the chillers by powering them up when energy is cheapest and shutting them down when it is more expensive.

So long as there is a decent volume of food in the chillers, optimum temperatures are maintained and no one notices the difference, except perhaps the finance department.

Other examples of time-shifted energy use would be the heating of swimming pools. Assuming a reasonable level of insulation, the bulk of heating the pool could be done at night when energy is cheap, with top-up heating cycles scheduled during the day to maintain the desired temperature.

PROJECT 10: REPLACE YOUR OLD GAS BOILERS

A large part of most companies' carbon footprint is associated with how they heat and cool their buildings. Many have old gas-fired or oil-burning boilers. Over time, boiler efficiency decreases, and technology improves (notably with the introduction of condensing boilers), meaning your old boiler may not be as efficient as it could be.

Year of installation	Efficiency (%)
1980-1984	59
1985-1989	61
1990-1994	71
1995-1999	73.5
2000-2004	81
2005-2009	87
2010-2014	89.5
2015-2019	91.5
2020-2023	94

Figure 43: *Typical energy efficiency of older boilers*[xxii].

You have two basic choices here: (a) replace the boiler with a newer model; or (b) replace or supplement the boiler with a high-efficiency heat pump[19]. When we look at the first option, this takes a fossil fuel burning piece of equipment and simply replaces it with a more efficient piece of equipment with the same inherent problem. Whilst this sounds sub-optimal and the case for heat pumps looks overwhelming, in practice you may find that heat pumps are either too expensive or do not provide the necessary temperature of water you need to heat your building without replacing large amounts of plumbing[20]. If you do replace your boilers, make sure you consider the control system for them and ensure that it has the ability to both control your heating remotely and turn the heating off automatically on holidays and weekends.

Heat pumps produce significantly less carbon emissions than gas boilers, making them a great option for companies looking to reduce their environmental impact. You will also see lower energy bills from heat pumps as they are highly efficient, with some models able to provide up to four times as much heat as the electricity they consume. If you can fit them, heat pumps are therefore a cleaner and cheaper choice in the long-term.

Other benefits of heat pumps over gas boilers are less obvious, but include:

- **Improved indoor air quality** – unlike gas boilers, which can emit harmful pollutants into the air, heat pumps do not produce any emissions that can negatively impact indoor air quality. This can be especially important for companies that have employees or customers who may have respiratory issues.
- **Longevity** – heat pumps tend to last longer than gas boilers, with an average lifespan of 15-25 years compared to around 10-15 years for gas boilers. This means that small companies can save money on maintenance and replacement costs in the long run.
- **Government incentives** – many governments offer incentives or tax credits for companies that install energy-efficient heating systems like heat pumps. By upgrading to a heat pump, small companies may be able to take advantage of these programmes and further reduce their costs.

19 Some people are not aware that air conditioning systems are heat pumps, so you may already have a heat pump without realising it.

20 Typical heat pump systems run cooler than boiler-driven systems meaning that, to maintain the same level of heating for your building, you may need to increase the size of your radiators. I have seen some heat pumps that claim to get around this issue, but at the time of writing, this certainly remains a problem.

When it comes to selecting a heat pump, there are two basic types: air source heat pumps and ground source heat pumps. Air source heat pumps are extremely common and the logical choice for most companies that do not have a large plot of land they can bury pipes in. Whichever you choose, a heat pump will lower your carbon footprint significantly more than installing a new gas or oil-based system.

PROJECT 11: REDUCE YOUR DEPENDENCE ON SINGLE USE PLASTICS

This is an interesting topic, because if you do the calculations on single-use plastics, they don't usually significantly contribute towards a company's carbon footprint. But that doesn't mean to say that they are not a problem, especially when we talk about the volume of plastics going into landfill and the ocean.

We ran an analysis of one 'eco-hotel' that very proudly packages its guest products (such as combs, nail files, toothbrushes and so on) in eco-friendly packaging. It also had large pump containers of shampoo and body wash instead of individual, single-use bottles. If the average person used two of those small plastic containers per day, these initiatives significantly lowered the amount of waste they sent to landfill. However, it only lowered their overall carbon footprint by 0.01%.

To reduce your single use plastics:

- **First, conduct an audit** of the business's current use of single-use plastics. Identify areas where single-use plastics are used and look for opportunities to switch to reusable alternatives.

- **Educate employees** about the environmental impact of single-use plastics and the importance of reducing their use. Encourage employees to use reusable water bottles, coffee cups and food containers.
- **Replace single-use plastics with reusable alternatives** wherever possible. This could include switching to reusable shopping bags, using refillable ink cartridges or purchasing reusable containers for food storage.
- **Work with suppliers** to reduce the amount of single-use plastics used in packaging and shipping. Encourage suppliers to use recyclable materials and reduce the amount of packaging used.
- **Monitor progress** regularly to track the reduction in single-use plastics and associated cost savings. Celebrate milestones and communicate progress to employees and customers to maintain momentum.

PROJECT 12: GREEN CHAMPIONS

Green champions are a great, cost-effective way of getting more people involved in your Net Zero project.

Having green champions in your company can bring a multitude of benefits. Firstly, they can help to raise awareness about environmental issues and promote sustainable practices within the workplace. This can lead to a more eco-friendly culture within the company, which not only benefits the environment but can also be a selling point for customers who prioritise sustainability and resonate with your new culture.

Secondly, green champions can help to identify opportunities for cost savings through more efficient use of resources and waste reduction. This can result in financial benefits for the company in the long-run.

Finally, having green champions can help attract and retain employees who are passionate about sustainability and want to work for a company that shares their values. Overall, having green champions can lead to a more environmentally conscious, financially efficient and socially responsible company.

Setting up and running an efficient green champion system in a company requires careful planning and execution:

1. **Identify and recruit green champions** – the first step is to identify employees who are passionate about sustainability and willing to take on the role of a green champion. It is important to ensure that they have the necessary skills and knowledge to lead green initiatives. Recruitment can be done through internal communications or by inviting employees to express their interest.
2. **Provide training and resources** – green champions should be provided with training on sustainability practices and resources to help them implement green initiatives. This can include access to research and data on sustainable practices, as well as communication materials (for example, posters and handouts) and technology that can help them track progress and measure results.
3. **Create a green action plan** – a green action plan should be created to outline the objectives and goals of the green champion system. This can include targets for reducing energy and water usage, waste reduction, and increasing the use of sustainable materials. The plan should be shared with all employees, and progress should be tracked and reported regularly.
4. **Encourage employee engagement** – employee engagement is critical to the success of the green champion system. Regular communication and engagement activities can help to raise awareness, promote sustainability and encourage participation. This can include activities such as sustainability-themed events, contests and incentives.

Setting up and running an efficient green champion system in a company can have significant benefits for both the environment and employees. By identifying and recruiting passionate and skilled employees, providing them with training and resources, creating a green action plan and encouraging employee engagement, companies can create a culture of sustainability and achieve their environmental goals.

A carbon treasure hunt

One fun activity to consider getting help with from your green champions is a carbon treasure hunt. In its most basic form:

- **Form a team** to conduct the carbon treasure hunt. It should include your green champions and any other relevant individuals.
- **Identify the scope** of the hunt, namely the areas within the company's operations that will be included. This can include buildings, transportation, manufacturing processes and supply chain.
- **Conduct an initial assessment** of the areas identified in the scope. This can involve collecting data on energy usage, water consumption, waste generation and transportation.
- **Set targets** for reducing the carbon footprint in each area based on the initial assessment. This can include targets for reducing energy usage, water consumption, waste generation and transportation emissions.
- **Conduct the treasure hunt**, with the aim of identifying areas where the company can reduce its carbon footprint. This can involve a physical inspection of buildings and equipment, as well as interviews with employees.
- **Analyse the results** by looking at the data collected to identify areas where the company can reduce its carbon footprint. This can include identifying opportunities for energy efficiency, water conservation, waste reduction and transportation emissions reduction.
- **Develop a plan** for reducing the company's carbon footprint based on the results of the carbon treasure hunt. This can involve implementing energy-efficient technologies, reducing water consumption, improving waste management practices and promoting sustainable transportation options.
- **Implement the plan**, with regular monitoring and reporting to track progress and ensure that targets are met.
- **Reward the team**, either formally or informally.

Funding and grants

As far as I can work out, UK government grants come in fits and spurts and are poorly managed. In one round of grants, we submitted six applications to improve the energy efficiency of heating systems in state schools, only to find that the entire £1.1 billion fund had already been allocated to a few large engineering conglomerates within 30 minutes of the application submission window opening. I hope that wherever you are based has better funding schemes and/or better management in place to ensure the money goes to where it's really needed.

Whilst I am seeing fewer and fewer government grants schemes becoming available these days, there are some interesting private funding schemes that are extremely popular that might help you fund your next project.

The easiest to understand are power purchase agreements (PPAs), which are usually used to fund renewable projects. Typically, a private fund will pay the upfront cost of a project, for example solar panels, so long as you commit to buying the energy they produce, at a subsidised rate, for the next 1020 years. If you don't want to use your own capital and have a suitable roof or field available, this arrangement can be beneficial for both parties.

Similarly, energy service companies (ESCOs) will often pay to upgrade old, inefficient equipment on the understanding that the savings that the upgraded equipment generates are shared fairly between them and you. For example, an old gas boiler is replaced with a modern combined heat and power plant for a cost of £1.2 million, which will generate a saving of £120,000 per year. The ESCO pays the £1.2 million on the understanding that they get half of the saving for the next 30 years.

Whilst both schemes can work well, they rely on accurate modelling at the outset and reliable measurement of the energy savings produced. The devil is very often in the detail, and if you consider using one of these schemes, I'd encourage you to be extremely thorough in checking the detail of the extensive contracts involved.

Chapter 10

TRACKING YOUR PROGRESS AND REVISING YOUR PLAN

Carbon Reduction Plan Section Five

HOW FREQUENTLY SHOULD YOUR CARBON REDUCTION PLAN BE UPDATED?

Your company circumstances and carbon use will hopefully change over time, with your carbon emissions reducing as you go. As such, you should update your plan periodically to reflect these changes and compare how well you are doing against the targets you set yourself initially. The frequency with which it's updated changes from company to company, but at the very least you should update your plan annually. If you are following the PPN 06/21 guidance, annual updates are also a requirement of the standard.

The data within your plan, however, should be constantly updated or, at the very least, on a monthly basis. By keeping on top of the data like this, if you spot any problems in the data you can jump on them and work to resolve them immediately. This approach significantly lowers the risk of not having the data you need. It is more likely that someone will have far easier access to the data you need from last month than from last year. This is especially true if staff changes are common in your company, as new staff are often less familiar with both the requirement for the data in the first place and where to locate it.

HOW TO ACCOUNT FOR GROWING OR SHRINKING COMPANIES USING CARBON INTENSITIES

If your company has changed size in the past year, you are probably going to hit a couple of snags when you start developing new editions of your Carbon Reduction Plan. Perhaps you have more staff, more floor space or possibly more production. Either way, it will mean that you can no longer compare the previous year's absolute carbon footprint to the current year as you are no longer comparing the same thing. The way around this is to abandon using absolute carbon emissions as your primary comparison metric, and instead switch over to using carbon intensities.

A carbon intensity is defined as the amount of carbon emitted per unit of activity.

Where:

- 'amount of carbon emitted' is tCO2e or kgCO2e; and
- 'unit of activity' is some objective measure in your business that you could use to represent the size or level of activity within your company.

Popular carbon intensities that we see regularly are:

- kgCO2e per £1 of turnover - the simplest and most popular carbon intensity. People like it because of the simplicity of calculation and because it makes comparing companies easy.
- kgCO2e per £1 profit generated - like the above, popular in larger companies and SBTi targets.
- kgCO2e per square foot - this is useful if your business turnover is related to the size of your premises, for example retail stores or storage rental businesses.
- tCO2e per employee - popular amongst fee earning companies where income is proportional to the number of advisors or consultants you have.
- kgCO2e per kg produced, or kgCO2 per item manufactured - a deceptively simple intensity favoured by manufacturing companies[21].

21 The complexity here lies in the fact that most manufacturers produce more than one product, and apportioning the overall carbon emissions to one product or another is sometimes difficult. You may, however, track several intensities, for example one for each product, which is perfectly acceptable.

- tCO_2e per tonne-mile delivered, or $kgCO_2e$ per passenger-mile - preferred for logistics companies and the transportation sector.
- $kgCO_2e$ per room night - favoured by hospitality companies.
- tCO_2e per pupil - used for schools.

As you can see, there are a variety of different ways you can express your carbon emission intensity and the method you choose is up to you[22] The golden rule is that whatever you choose should be proportional to some degree to the size of your business. Focussing on the intensity, rather than the absolute emissions, therefore, allows you to account for changes in the size of your organisation from year to year.

Carbon intensities in the real world

Gloria runs a pharmaceutical company. Due to Brexit, she has recently had to open a new factory in Germany to get around European Union rules that make it harder for UK companies to sell drugs into Europe. This has been successful, and the overall quantity of pills she is selling has increased by 87% since 2017.

Her carbon footprint for producing 1.4 billion pills in 2016 was 3,171 tCO_2e, but with her new operation in Germany her carbon footprint in 2022 was 4,921 tCO_2e for 2.6 billion pills.

Gloria's carbon footprint has increased in that time by 55%, which may seem bad at first glance. However, her carbon intensity was:

2016: 0.000002265 tCO_2e per pill = 0.002265 $kgCO_2e$ per pill = 2.3 $kgCO_2e$ per 1,000 pills

2022: 0.000001893 tCO_2e per pill = 0.001893 $kgCO_2e$ per pill = 1.9 $kgCO_2e$ per 1,000 pills

Her carbon intensity therefore reduced by 17% during this period. This can be attributed to many things, but in particular to: (a) newer equipment in her new factory; and (b) lower distribution costs, as many of the pills are now manufactured closer to where they are being sold.

Due to the changing nature of Gloria's operations, carbon intensity is therefore a more appropriate measure of her carbon emissions than absolute emission levels.

---

22 I suspect that different industry sectors may end up with their own de facto standards for what to choose, such as 'tCO_2e per tonne produced' for the steel industry.

You can track multiple intensities and mix them for your business. For example, for an airport:

- X $kgCO_2e$ per passenger served in ground operations; and
- Y $kgCO_2e$ per passenger mile for airside operations.

Be careful, however, that when reporting these numbers to people who have less time or interest in the calculation, you don't use too many intensities. Often, people prefer to have one intensity to focus on, rather than trying to digest a set of sometimes conflicting metrics.

Progress against these targets can be seen in the graph below:

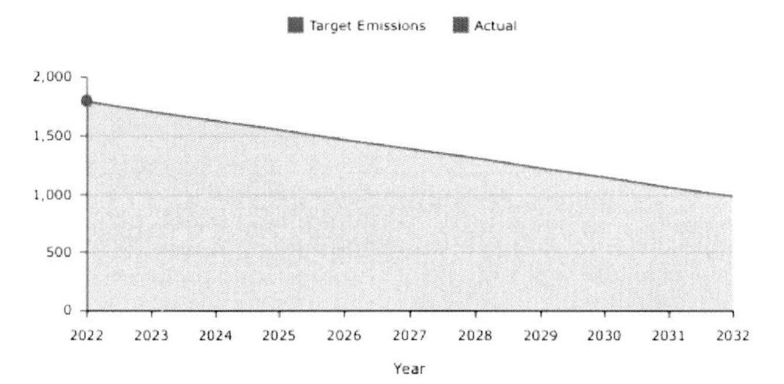

Carbon Reduction Projects

Completed Carbon Reduction initiatives

The following environmental management measures and projects have been completed or implemented since the 2022 baseline. The carbon emission reduction achieved by these schemes equate to 776 tCO_2e, a 45%ge reduction against the 2022 baseline and the measures will be in effect when performing the contract.

Realtime Telematics

In 2017, we were the first large fleet to install Lightfoot in-cab technology on our van fleet, empowering our drivers to be energy efficient whilst still maintaining high standards and delivery times. The telematics system provides real-time feedback to drivers so they can adjust their behaviours immediately. To date, we have saved 1,279 tonnes of CO2e whilst also increasing safe driving

Sustainable products and solutions

We're making it easier for our customers to improve their energy efficiency through smarter technology. Our Smart Home offering is helping people make their homes or office more efficient by providing them with the data and tools they need to make sustainable choices. As well as saving time, the enhancements to heating, lighting, security make for a more comfortable and environmentally friendly solution.

Figure 44: A typical carbon reduction tracking page. This screen is taken from Yeti and also shows the first part of the carbon reduction projects section.

PLANNING FOR THE FUTURE – REVISING YOUR CARBON REDUCTION PLAN

As you prepare your Carbon Reduction Plan, you are going to come across problems with your data. Perhaps some of the data you need isn't complete, or maybe it is simply not available to you. This is particularly true when it comes to getting accurate and consistent data for your supply chain. These problems are common, and they are sometimes the type of problem that you can't fix overnight.

Keep a list of which areas of your plan could be revised and for each deficiency, list a sentence or two about how that area can be improved in future and what timescales you think these improvements might be made over. A good way to represent this is using a data quality RAG (red, amber, green) report, as shown below.

Data item	2021	2022	2023	Notes
Electricity				
Gas				
Company car fuel				
Staff mileage				This area is still problematic. Our expenses system needs to be changed to include the data fields we need.
Supply chain				Getting reliable data from the supplier is still problematic but is improving. Our new carbon portal is helping here.
Flights				
Hotels				
Trains				An initiative with the finance department to include these items on expenses is being trialled.
Waste				A new waste supplier who can provide more accurate data is being sourced.
Deliveries in				
Deliveries out				
Commuting				We are pleased to say that participation in the latest staff survey was over 50%.

Figure 45: *A data quality matrix showing how good your data is and highlighting any areas that need attention.*

Chapter 11

OFFSETS AND REMOVALS

Carbon Reduction Plan Section Six

WHAT ARE OFFSETS?

As you progress down your Net Zero journey, you are going to reduce your carbon use down to the absolute minimum. You're going to do every cost-justified project you can possibly think of to lower your carbon footprint and do the right thing for the planet. But, every year, you're still going to end up with some carbon emissions that you simply can't get rid of, no matter how hard you try.

Every company, without exception, will have this problem. Every time you go anywhere, you're going to emit carbon. Every time you buy something, you will cause emissions to be generated by the supplier. Every time you use electricity or gas, you're going to emit carbon, even if it comes from renewables (after all, somebody must build, buy, install and maintain those solar panels). No matter what you do, you will always end up with a block of carbon that you cannot reduce any further.

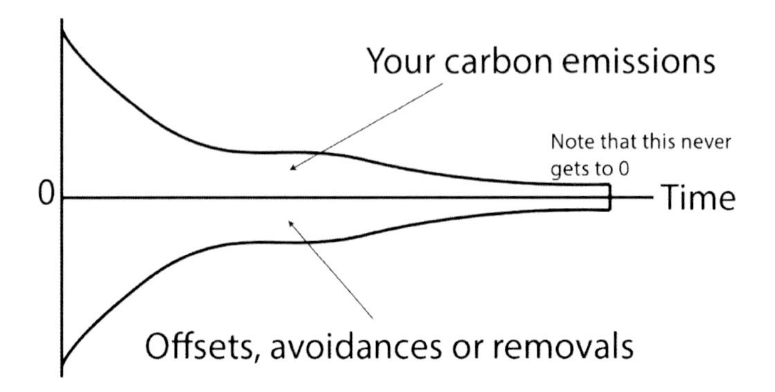

Figure 47: Using offsets, avoidances and removals to reduce your overall carbon impact to zero

The way we handle this block of carbon that we can't get rid of is either through removals, offsetting or avoidance:

- **Removals** – there are a small number of companies that have machines to suck the CO_2 from the atmosphere and lock it up long-term, typically deep underground. For example, Climeworks in Iceland sucks CO_2 from the atmosphere and locks it away in geological faults.
- **Offsetting** - this usually involves finding a company that is doing something worthy to reduce the carbon footprint of the planet and helping to fund its activity. For example, paying someone to plant trees for you.
- **Avoidance** - either buying some equipment that someone can use to avoid them generating the emissions they would otherwise have created or paying for a carbon reducing project not to be degraded. For example, by buying someone a solar cooker in rural Africa, you avoid them having to burn wood when they cook, thus avoiding carbon emissions, or paying someone not to cut down a forest.

REMOVALS, OFFSETS OR AVOIDANCE?

Let's look at these three options in more detail.

REMOVALS

Removals are exactly what we all want. The process usually involves a large processing plant that sucks the CO_2 out of the atmosphere using a reversible chemical reaction and fans, and then stores this deep underground in rock fissures.

Although large amounts of government funding are going into improving the technology, these plants are still very expensive to run. As I write, typical costs for an offset scheme are around £30 per tonne, whereas removal costs are £1,200 per tonne.

OFFSETS

Removal systems may be our preference, but they're very expensive and there aren't many of them. What people turn to instead are offset schemes.

Offset schemes work by paying volunteers, companies or charities to do things which 'negate' your carbon emissions, for example, planting trees. These projects have a negative carbon footprint impact, and by funding them, you are allowing them to do more good work and offset an additional amount of carbon dioxide in the process. It relies heavily on the principal if additionality, i.e. *"Without your donation, these additional trees would not have been planted"*. For example, a typical tree will absorb 0.01 tonnes of CO_2 per year[xxiii], so to offset a carbon footprint of 7 tCO_2e per year you would need to plant: 7 / 0.01 = 700 trees per year.[23]

A note on terminology

Confusingly, 'offset schemes' refers to 'removals', 'avoidances' and 'offsets'. I understand that there is an element of double definition here and that we should really call this something less confusing, but we don't.

In this book, if you see the term 'offsets', it generally refers to any of these three sub-categories interchangeably.

Planting trees to offset emissions is a bit like buying Catholic indulgences in the 12th century. If you were an evil miscreant, you could go to the Catholic

23 A rule of thumb is 1,000 trees per hectare, so we would need to plant 0.7 hectares of trees each year, or the size of a UK football pitch.

Church and pay to have those sins of absolved[24]. In the same way, your company could simply buy carbon offsets to negate its emissions, and suddenly in the eyes of the world, you are now 'green'. Throughout this book, I therefore tightly couple the concept of certified Net Zero with *reducing your emissions as much as possible and offsetting what is left*. Using offsets on their own is therefore not a method by which to achieve Net Zero[25].

AVOIDANCE

The third method of offsetting your carbon emissions is through avoidance schemes. They are like offset schemes, but instead of contributing to the absorption of CO_2, they avoid it being emitted in the first place.

Examples of an avoidance scheme would be solar cookers. They don't lock up any CO_2 as would a removal scheme; in fact, you must manufacture the cooker in the first place, which will generate CO_2. However, they will avoid emission of CO_2 over the longer term.

The argument goes that each cooker prevents approximately 3 tCO_2e per year[xxiv] by using solar energy to cook rather than burning wood. If each cooker costs £1,000 to make and has a lifespan of 10 years, they can therefore save 30 tCO_2e for £1,000, resulting in an avoidance scheme cost of 0.03 tCO_2e per £1.

Avoidances schemes where people are paid not to do something, for example paying someone not to cut down a forest, are open to abuse (see below) and the validity of the claims should be examined extremely carefully if you are considering funding them.

---

24 Interestingly, you could also buy these indulgences in advance, which is a rather troublesome concept.

25 As I write, the European Union has also just passed a law to prohibit companies calling themselves 'green' as a result of buying offsets. There is more clarity on the details of this to come, but this is a definite step in the right direction.

Offsets

Seaweed Farming Innovation, Cornwall

This project is an opportunity to invest in early stage, nature-based innovation and help write the science to scale up seaweed farming across the South West of the UK.

£36 / tonne

More

Peatland Protection, Rimba Raya

The Rimba Raya Biodiversity Reserve project is protecting one of the most highly endangered ecosystems in the world. Without this project, the carbon-rich, peatland forest of Rimba Raya would have been turned into palm oil estates...

£12.03 / tonne

More

Dryland Protection, Kasigau Wildlife Corridor

The Kasigau Corridor project is a REDD+ project based in Rukinga, Kenya. It protects an expanse of over 200,000 hectares of dryland Acacia-Commiphora forest home to over 2,000 elephants.

£19 / tonne

More

Figure 48: A typical offset purchase page from an online system. This screen is taken from Yeti.

LIFETIME EMISSIONS

When we look at our offsetting requirements, there are two ways of considering the problem. The first is to say, *"We're going to offset our annual carbon footprint"*, and the second is to consider offsetting what's called 'lifetime emissions'. This is the amount of emissions your company has caused to be emitted since it was first established.

There are many ways of calculating what your emissions were since incorporation, none of them very accurate, but the most common is to assume that the growth of the company has been linear since incorporation and add up emissions over the years based on this. Of course, if you have a better measure of your growth by using, for example, the annual turnover since incorporation[26], then by all means use that.

One way of approaching lifetime emissions is to look at offsetting all annual emissions plus 10% of the excess lifetime emissions. This means that in 10 years, your lifetime emissions will be fully negated and yet, at the same time, it keeps the costs of doing so manageable.

It's true to say that not many of our clients choose to offset their lifetime emissions, but those that do can generate a good marketing story and a degree of one-upmanship over their competitors.

PROBLEMS WITH OFFSETS AND ABUSE OF THE SYSTEM

When we deal with offsets, we must be very careful. There are a number of potential traps that you can fall into unless you are cautious and do your research. I've listed here some of the things to look out for, and when you come to offset, please follow the advice at the end of this section regarding how to choose offsets accredited by a reliable standard[27].

CORRUPTION

There are people who invent fictitious carbon offsets. They do this by generating one certificate after another for the same carbon offsets for the same project. Without robust standards to protect the buyer, they are able to sell the same offsets for a fictitious project repeatedly.

PROFITEERING

Another problem is profiteering, in which people abuse the system by twisting the truth and misrepresenting it to their advantage. For example,

---

26 Adjusted for inflation and prevalence of modern equipment such as IT, machinery, transport systems and so on.

27 I was asked by someone in 2022 how to set up a carbon offsetting standard, how to set up a carbon exchange to trade carbon offsets and how to register a 10 hectare field on both systems to profit from selling carbon offsets. He had no intention whatsoever of doing anything remotely carbon-friendly with the land, and whilst I declined to help, there is, unfortunately, no oversight body that would prevent him doing this. The system is open to abuse, and most definitely is being abused by some.

being paid not to cut down trees when there was no intention of ever doing it in the first place.

In theory, if a company intends to cut down a forest and use it for legitimate farming purposes, a conscientious carbon investor would pay the landowner the profit that they would otherwise have generated from farming that field on the condition that they leave the forest intact. The fraud occurs here when there was no real intention of ever cutting the forest down in the first place, and landowners simply claim there was to get the payout.

The way around this fraud is to only buy offsets from a reputable source and make sure robust standards are in place for the offsets you wish to buy.

POORLY DESIGNED PROJECTS

It is also worth addressing the problems of poorly designed projects, such as monoculture afforestation projects. Typically, these are where spruce trees are uniquely used to repopulate an area.

Yes, the trees will grow and lock away carbon, but the forests that result lack biodiversity and will not flourish in the manner that you might expect. This problem is exacerbated if the species chosen, for example spruce, is not a species that is natural to the area, such as might occur if you chose to plant 10 hectares of bamboo forest in central London.

The offset project owners will make promises about how the forest will grow and thrive and lock away carbon, creating a rich, fertile environment for nature to regain a foothold. In reality, the offsets that they priced up and sold at the outset will never really develop the biodiversity promised.

INTERNATIONAL STANDARDS ARE WEAK

There are only a few certifying bodies out there that are truly beyond reproach, and there is nothing to help the average buyer distinguish between them, nor any centralised agency to police them.

The international standards in this area are weak and require re-evaluating. For example, there's nothing stopping you creating your own carbon exchange with your own set of standards and profiting from people not knowing that the '1,000 AAA-rated, Grade 1 Carbon Offsets (Project ref: 318-72A)' and the 'International Carbon Rating Institute of Oxford' are in fact purely fictitious and not worth the paper they are written on.

ADDITIONALITY

Another major problem with offsets is that of additionality, which is one of the underlying assumptions behind offsetting. The concept is that:

- *"Without your investment of £X, Y tCO2e of carbon would not have been locked away, avoided or removed."*
- For example, compare the following two scenarios:
- *"Without your investment of £10,000 in our scheme to replant two hectares of forest outside of our village and lock away carbon for generations, it would not have happened."*
- *"We were going to replant the area outside of our school anyway. We have the funds, it's just better for us if we use your money to do it and not ours."*

You can see that your investment into the second scheme would not change anything - it would not create any more carbon savings than were already going to happen without your investment[28]. As such, it fails the additionality test.

OFFSETS WITHOUT REDUCTIONS

The last problem to consider is the Catholic indulgences problem we spoke about above. You *must* reduce your carbon footprint as much as possible and *only then* offset what emissions still remain. Too many companies buy offsets and claim to be Net Zero when they haven't changed their working practices at all and have not sufficiently considered a long-term plan to reduce their emissions to as near to zero as possible. Offsets should be considered one of the final steps in any carbon reduction journey, not a quick-win alternative to making legitimate reductions.

HOW TO SELECT THE HIGHEST QUALITY OFFSET PROJECTS

It's important to avoid 'dodgy' offsets. There are many of them out there with the sorts of problems we've highlighted above.

28 I'm always dubious when I see carbon offset schemes based on putting up acres of new wind turbines or selling offsets generated by new hydro-electric dams. Perhaps I shouldn't be so cynical, but I can't help but think that some of these schemes would have gone ahead anyway, regardless of any donations.

There are two things to consider when assessing an offset scheme: (a) what standards is it certified under; and (b) who is selling it. In terms of standards, it varies from country to country, but at Enistic we use Gold Standard. There are others, but with a busy workload and many clients to help, we always use this.

In terms of who is selling them, you should consider what formal standards they have (for example, ISO 9000, ISO 14000), who is behind the company, what their reviews are like and how long they have been in operation for. A new company with few standards and unknown private backers is probably best avoided in the short-term.

MAXIMISING THE BENEFITS OF OFFSETTING

If you're on a Net Zero path, you will be looking at reducing your carbon footprint to the absolute minimum and using offsets to negate what's left. At around £30 per tCO2e at the time of writing, this can be relatively expensive, and if you are going to be making this investment you should try and get the most out of it.

First, this is a great opportunity to engage your staff in your Net Zero journey. Start by selecting three offset schemes from the broad list of available categories.

For example:

- A local scheme that benefits your immediate area by supporting tree planting in the local neighbourhood
- A national scheme that subsidises the provision of low-carbon heating systems to the less fortunate
- An international scheme that provides solar cookers in rural Africa

Next, with an indication of the amount of offset funding available and some engaging images to showcase the projects, ask your staff and/or other stakeholders to vote on what they would like to see the company support. Perhaps because of the imagery involved, this step is the single biggest area that people can relate to. Whilst it may be significantly beneficial for you to upgrade the insulation in your exterior walls, it simply doesn't get people as fired up as pictures of rainforests being repopulated.

Second, what you will be doing here is a charitable and altruistic activity. You will be donating money to a just and worthy cause and can quite rightly use this in your company communications in the same manner as you might do with any other charitable donations you make.

For example,

> *"Joanne's cupcakes – supporting the rewilding of rural Uganda. Find out more about how we're supporting ..."*

Chapter 12

CERTIFICATION AND COMMITMENT

Carbon Reduction Plan Section Seven

WHAT IS CERTIFICATION?

Certification is asking a third party to review your Carbon Reduction Plan, taking a close look at the data you've put in, the assumptions you've made and the calculations you've carried out to verify that they meet the required detail and quality.

The concept of certification for Net Zero is new, and it might be that it will not catch on. You may, therefore, struggle to find a reputable certification agency. Self-certification is a possibility, but may be viewed in a negative light by prospective readers of your plan. Hopefully, more companies will enter the certification sector to widen the choice available.

Certification is a valuable process that provides checks and balances for the sector. It allows one Carbon Reduction Plan to be compared with another in the knowledge that the same things are being measured in the same manner from company to company.

On a very personal level, another benefit of certification is that someone else will spend time looking through *your* calculations and give what you have done their stamp of approval. Many people are not confident when they produce their first Carbon Reduction Plan, and getting someone to double check it gives you a reassuring nod that it has been done correctly.

PREPARING FOR CERTIFICATION: THE CERTIFICATION CHECKLIST

It is important to do as much as you can to make sure you pass certification first time, to keep costs and disruption to a minimum. Here are seven things that you should check before you apply for certification.

1 - DOES THE CARBON FOOTPRINT INCLUDE THE REQUIRED ELEMENTS?

The first thing to check is that your carbon footprint is measured and has all the required components. For Net Zero, this includes all emissions resulting from use of electricity, gas and other fuels, your supply chain, the deliveries you make and receive, staff travel, commuting, working from home, business travel, hotels and waste.

2 - ARE THE REQUIRED ELEMENTS PROCESSED TO THE NECESSARY ACCURACY?

Your data accuracy is the next thing to consider. Accuracy for Scope 1 and Scope 2 for some UK standards is typically around the 97% mark, but for Net Zero anything over 90% is acceptable. We know that Scope 3 data is more problematic, and anything greater than 60% accuracy should be acceptable.

3 - IS THE DATA FOR THE CORRECT PERIOD?

The next thing to look for is whether your data covers the correct time period, typically the previous financial year.

4 - WERE THE CALCULATIONS DONE CORRECTLY?

If you have chosen not to use a software package to calculate your carbon footprint, double check that your calculations have been done correctly, particularly that the correct carbon factors have been applied.

Don't forget that most factors change annually and vary by location, so it is also important to check that the correct carbon factors for the relevant time period and country have been used.

5 - ARE THERE AIMS AND TARGETS STATED, AND ARE THEY SUFFICIENTLY AMBITIOUS?

Check whether your aims and targets are clearly stated and whether they are sufficiently ambitious. Look for one target based around 2030 (or before) and a second, more ambitious target of, say, a 95% reduction in emissions by 2045 or 2050[29].

6 - IS THERE A CREDIBLE PLAN TO REDUCE THE FOOTPRINT?

Review which carbon reduction projects you have committed to in the plan. Consider two aspects: (a) whether they include the basics, such as LED lighting, video conferencing and so on; and (b) whether some of the projects included are specifically relevant to your industry sector[30].

7 - IS THERE A TRACKING SECTION SHOWING PROGRESS OVER TIME?

For the progress and tacking section, you are generally looking for a graph of progress over time, showing both what your emissions were year-on-year and what you had planned for them to be. If they differ, ensure that there is some commentary about the reasons for this and any remedial actions you have considered as a result.

8 - ARE THERE PLANS FOR THE EMISSIONS THAT CANNOT BE ELIMINATED TO BE OFFSET, AND ARE THOSE OFFSETS CREDIBLE?

The offsets area is simple to check. Look at whether you are offsetting the entire amount of carbon emissions that you have not managed to otherwise eliminate, and make sure the offset projects you have selected conform to a recognised standard.

---

29 Recognising that most long-term plans are based more on hopes and aspirations for dramatic future technology improvements rather than on practical reduction plans.

30 This is mentioned in PPN 06/21, although I have not seen many plans that specifically go out of their way to emphasise these.

9 - IS THERE SIGN-OFF BY A SENIOR DIRECTOR?

Make sure the plan has been signed off by a company director, or a trustee if you are a charity.

10 - IS THE DOCUMENT PUBLISHED PROMINENTLY ON THE COMPANY WEBSITE?

Finally, ensure that the plan itself is published publicly on your website and that there is a link to it on your homepage. In theory, according to PPN 06/21 this link should be 'prominent', but if it exists and is not hidden, I suspect most certification agencies will be happy.

HOW LONG DOES IT TAKE TO GET CERTIFIED?

The length of time it takes to get certified varies considerably depending on the certifying body you select, but 5-10 working days is typical.

Declaration and Sign Off

This Carbon Reduction Plan has been completed in accordance with PPN 06/21 and associated guidance and reporting standard for Carbon Reduction Plans.

Emissions have been reported and recorded in accordance with the published reporting standard for Carbon Reduction Plans and the GHG Reporting Protocol corporate standard[1] and uses the appropriate Government emission conversion factors for greenhouse gas company reporting[2].

Scope 1 and Scope 2 emissions have been reported in accordance with SECR requirements, and the required subset of Scope 3 emissions have been reported in accordance with the published reporting standard for Carbon Reduction Plans and the Corporate Value Chain (Scope 3) Standard[3].

This Carbon Reduction Plan has been reviewed and signed off by the board of directors (or equivalent management body).

Signed on behalf of the Supplier:

....

Date: ....

[1] https://ghgprotocol.org/corporate-standard
[2] https://www.gov.uk/government/collections/government-conversion-factors-for-company-reporting
[3] https://ghgprotocol.org/standards/scope-3-standard

Figure 49: A typical director sign-off page in a Carbon Reduction Plan. This page is taken from Yeti.

Chapter 13

AND FINALLY ...

Congratulations! By now, you should have a fully compliant Carbon Reduction Plan. The next question is, what should you do with it now to maximise the benefits of all that work?

First, identify relevant stakeholders to be sent the plan. Some of the groups to consider are:

- **Major clients** – along with the message: *"Look what we're doing. We're proud of our environmental achievements to date and we've got some ambitious plans to reduce our carbon footprint even further and become certified Net Zero by [2030]".*
- **Staff –** some of whom will hopefully have had input into the plan either directly or via green champions, green teams and ubiquitous online suggestion boxes.
- **Investors** – there are many eco-restrictions on larger investors these days, and there's certainly a growing desire for them to invest in the *"right sorts of companies"*. This is your opportunity to show investors that your company is indeed one of these companies.
- **The general public** – publish your plan on your website with a link from the homepage. This is your chance to tell the outside world: *"This is what we're doing. We care about the environment, and we have a transparent and coherent plan in place to do our bit to help tackle the problems we all face today".*

Finally, look to put the highlights of your Carbon Reduction Plan in your company's annual report, or link to the entire plan from your annual accounts. If you're a UK company above a certain size, there is a requirement in Streamlined Energy and Carbon Reporting Regulation (SECR) that you publish your carbon footprint highlights and include them in your annual accounts.

Appendix 1

ACKNOWLEDGMENTS

I'd like to thank my wonderful wife, Sally, for her hard work helping me edit this book; Elizabeth who very carefully read through it all and pointed out sections that could be improved; and Farrah & Silvia who provided much needed design help and advice throughout.

If it's even possible, I'd like to 'thank' the AI system Midjourney for providing the illustrations in the book. Most of the illustrations were designed from prompts that include the phrase *"in the style of ..."* and then a name chosen from a selection of my favourite artists. If you want a challenge, try identifying which artist style was used for each illustration. Bonus points if you can identify the Lichtensteins from the Warhols and Monets.

Appendix 2

BIBLIOGRAPHY AND REFERENCES

i https://www.cdp.net/en/research/global-reports/global-climate-change-report-2019, retrieved 7 Jan 2023

ii https://www.nielsen.com/wp-content/uploads/sites/3/2018/10/global-responsibility-report-oct-2018.pdf, retrieved 7 May 2023

iii https://www.conecomm.com/research-blog/2017-csr-study, retrieved 7 May 2023

iv https://www.accenture.com/_acnmedia/PDF-77/Accenture-Strategy-Global-Consumer-Study.pdf, retrieved 7 May 2023

v https://ec.europa.eu/clima/policies/ets_en, retrieved 7 May 2023

vi https://www.conecomm.com/research-blog/2016-millennial-employee-engagement-study, retrieved 7 May 2023

vii https://www.cdp.net/en/research/global-reports/global-supply-chain-report-2019, retrieved 12 December 2022

viii https://www.carbontrust.com/media/23480/ctc837-the-business-benefits-of-a-sustainable-supply-chain.pdf, retrieved 7 May 2023

ix https://www.morganstanley.com/content/dam/msdotcom/infographics/sustainable-investing/Sustainable_Realities_2021.pdf, retrieved 7 May 2023

x https://www.heathrow.com/content/dam/heathrow/web/common/documents/company/heathrow-2-0-sustainability/Heathrow_SustainabilityReport2022.pdf, retrieved on 1 April 2023

xi https://www.worldometers.info/co2-emissions/co2-emissions-by-country/, retrieved on 26 March 2023.

xii https://www.gov.uk/government/publications/greenhouse-gas-reporting-conversion-factors-2022, retrieved on 2 November 2022 xiii https://www.news-medical.net/health/Impact-of-Chocolate-on-our-Climate.aspx#:~:text=Indeed%2C%20an%20average%2040%2Dgram,of%20its%20greater%20cacao%20content, retrieved 1 April 2023

xiv https://www.gov.uk/government/publications/greenhouse-gas-reporting-conversion-factors-2022, retrieved 24 May 2023

xv https://www.transitionpathwayinitiative.org/publications/32.pdf?type=Publication#:~:text=Therefore%2C%20the%20average%20carbon%20intensity,per%20tonne%20of%20aluminium%20produced, retrieved 1 May 2023

xvi https://enistic.earth/, retrieved 24 May 2023

xvii https://www.bbc.co.uk/news/science-environment-63089348, retrieved 13 May 2023

xviii https://www.world-nuclear.org/information-library/energy-and-the-environment/carbon-dioxide-emissions-from-electricity.aspx, retrieved 10 April 2023.

xix Source: DEFRA 2020 report and EPA GHG Emission Factors Hub 2021

xx https://www.plasticsoupfoundation.org/en/plastic-problem/bogus-solutions/recycling-myth/?gclid=CjwKCAjwjYKjBhB5EiwAiFdSfqYtMdVkGgApL4cIcu1qPEhcUIezCGpbBiRFOWT7kfoCuiHmgB2DixoCfzQQAvD_BwE, retrieved 15 May 2023

xxi https://www.whatprice.co.uk/travel/train-prices.html, retrieved on 12 April 2023

xxii Collated by Chat GPT on 20 December 2022

xxiii https://onetreeplanted.org/blogs/stories/how-much-co2-does-tree-absorb, retrieved 24 April 2023

xxiv https://unfccc.int/climate-action/momentum-for-change/activity-database/momentum-for-change-the-mekhe-solar-cooker-project, retrieved 24 April 2023